THE BEST BOOK OF FOOTBALL SONGS

Ever!

SEVENOAKS

CONTENTS

INTRODUCTION

I can't remember the first time I went to a football match, except to say it would have been in the early 1970s. Similarly, I'm sure I'm not the only football fan who finds it all too easy to forget what has happened in most matches I watch (4–3 thrillers excepted) within a day or two.

It's because most matches are so depressingly ordinary they fail to leave an impression. Of course, you can remember the score, the scorers, how the goals were scored and the other important bits, but most of it will have drifted into the wastebasket of our memories within a very short space of time. Not so the chants and songs. We've all got our favourites, but the ones which really stick in our minds can often come from an unlikely source – the opposing fans.

You know the kind of thing. Your side's playing rubbish, so badly that they can't see off the worst excuse of a football team that they've played in years; it's blowing a gale and chucking it down; the half-time pies were rubbish and none of the players look capable of scoring in a nightclub let alone on the pitch – and then, all of a sudden, the supporters of the other team belt out, 'We're s*** and we're sick of it' (and it's only October).

Now not only does that give us all a bit of a laugh but here we have, in one simple line, a succinct and definitive expression of what those fans think of being treated to such a crap display when they've taken a half-day off to travel halfway across the country for the second leg of a cup competition that changes its name once a season.

And though we might have a good laugh at their expense, there is a serious side to all this vocal hilarity. Their frustration could be borne of terminally inept boardroom members, a manager who can't tell his League Two from his Champions League or players desperately short on talent.

But what effect do the chanting have? Well, the players certainly hear it, as does the management and whichever board members have bothered to show up. Surely, it prompts some reaction in them. I hope so, because it's the fans who create the atmosphere and they have a right to respect from the clubs they support. If they stopped going, where would the game be?

In compiling this book I've tried to reflect the contemporary and the best of yesteryear while attempting to retain a sense of originality for each club. However, with all the best will in the world, some clubs' fans do lack imagination, and they tend to be the ones which also lack success. Some were able to supply only the flimsiest of offerings for this collection. Indeed, Bury told me they had no supporters' club and no fanzine, which goes to confirm what we Bolton fans have known about them for years: S**t ground, no fans!

David Hulmes, London

ENGLISH FOOTBALL CLUBS

ARSENAL

We've Got That Double Feeling
(To the tune of 'You've Lost That Loving Feeling')
We've got that Double feeling
Oohh, that Double feeling
We've got that Double feeling
'Cos it's on, on, on ...

Arsenal Chant (1)
One nil to the Arsenal
One nil to the Arsenal

Arsène Wenger's Magic
Arsène Wenger's magic
He wears a magic hat
And when he saw the double
He said I'm having that
Oooooo!
(repeat)

Let's Talk About Cesc Baby
Let's talk about Cesc baby
Let's talk about Flamini
Let's talk about Theo Walcott, Freddie Ljungberg and Henry
Let's talk about Cesc baby
(Adapted from Salt 'n' Pepa's 'Let's Talk About Sex Baby')

Arsenal Chant (2)
We'll win, 'cos we're Arsenal

Classic Nicolas Anelka Chant
La, la, la, la, la, la An-el-ka
La, la, la, la, la, la An-el-ka
La, la, la, la, la, la An-el-ka
La, la, la, la, la, la An-el-ka

Classic Emmanuel Petit Chant (1) *(pre-World Cup)*
He's blond, he's quick
His name's a porno flick
Emmanuel, Emmanuel

Classic Emmanuel Petit Chant (2)*(post-World Cup)*
He's quick, he's blond
He won the Coup du Monde
Emmanuel, Emmanuel

Always S*** On the West Side of the Thames
Always s*** on the west side of the Thames
da da da da da da da da da da
Always s*** on the west side of the Thames
da da da da da da da da da da
(Sung to Chelsea fans)

She Wore a Yellow Ribbon

She wore, she wore, she wore a yellow ribbon
She wore a yellow ribbon
In the merry month of May
And when I asked her why she wore that ribbon
She said it's for the Arsenal
And we're going to Wem-ber-lee
Wem-ber-lee Wem-ber-lee
We're the famous Ar-se-nal
And we're going to Wem-ber-lee

Arsenal Chant (3)

Boring, boring Arsenal!
*(Sung by the North Bank when Arsenal
are winning comprehensively)*

Back to London

Back to London
We'll Race you back to London
Baaaaaack to London
*(Sung to Manchester United fans at Old Trafford,
many of whom are not actually from Manchester)*

We Love You Arsenal, We Do

(To the tune of 'I'm H.A.P.P.Y')

We love you Arsenal, we do,

We love you Arsenal, we do,

We love you Arsenal, we do,

Oh Arsenal we love you!

Arsenal till I die,

I'm Arsenal till I die

I know I am,

I'm sure I am,

I'm Arsenal till I die...

Classic Teddy Sheringham Chant
Oooooo, Teddy, Teddy
He went to Man United
And he won f*** all
You'll win f*** all again
Sheringham, Sheringham

Classic Dennis Bergkamp Wonderland
One Dennis Bergkamp
There's only one Dennis Bergkamp
Walking along, singing a song
Walking in a Bergkamp wonderland

We Got the Best Player in the World
We got the best player in the world,
We got the best player in the world,
We got the best player in the world,
We got the best player in the world,
HENRY!
(An accolade to Thierry)

One Man and his Dog
One man went to laugh, went to laugh at Chelsea
One man and his dog (Spot), went to laugh at Chelsea
(repeat up to ten men)

Classic Patrick Vieira Chant
He comes from Senegal
He plays for Arsenal
Vieira, o-o-o-o-oh Vieira (etc.)

Arsenal Chant (4)
Hark now, hear the Arsenal sing
The Tottenham run away
And we will fight forever more
Because of Boxing Day

ASTON VILLA

Classic Dwight Yorke Chant
(To the tune of 'New York, New York')
Start spreading the news
He's playing today
I want to see him score again
Dwight Yorke, Dwight Yorke

If he can (pause) score from there
He'll score from (pause) anywhere
It's up to you
Dwight Yorke, Dwight Yorke
De de, dedede, de de dedede
*(obviously not sung since "Yorkie"
left to play for Manchester United)*

You Are My Sunshine
You are my Villa, my only Villa,
You make me happy, when skies are grey
I never notice how much I love you
Until they take my Villa away

Roll Along

Roll along, Aston Villa, roll along
To the top of the League where you belong
There'll be cups and trophies too
For the boys in Claret 'n' Blue
Roll along, Aston Villa, roll along

Sing When We're Shopping

Sing when we're shopping, we only sing when
we're shopping
*(In the away end at Bolton's former home,
Burnden Park)*

Classic John Carew Chant

John Carew, Carew
He likes a lap-dance or two
He might even pay for you
John Carew, Carew
*(Sung to the tune of 'Que Sera Sera' by Doris Day,
this was the fans' tribute after Carew was caught
visiting a gentlemen's club)*

A Footballer Called Dwight Yorke
(To the tune of 'An Englishman In New York')
When he's on the pitch at Villa Park
And he's really on his game
He can twist and turn and score a goal!
Everybody knows his name!

Ooooooooooo, he's a footballer
An Aston Villa footballer
He's a footballer called Dwight Yorke

Classic "Steve Bruce, Are You listening?" Chant
Steve Bruce, are you listening?
To the song we are singing
We're walking along, singing this song
S***ting on the City when we go
*(To the tune of 'Winter Wonderland', this was sung
when Birmingham City signed Steve Bruce)*

Sign On

(To the tune of 'You'll Never Walk Alone' when playing Liverpool)

Sign on, sign on
With a pen in your hand
'Cos you'll ne-ver work a-gain
You'll ne-ver work again
Sign on, sign on

Go Once A Season

Go once a season
You only go once a season
Go once a season
(to Man Utd and Liverpool)

Glory, Glory Aston Villa

My eyes have seen the glory of the Villa win the Cup,
seven times we've won it and we need to back it up!
we are the boys in Claret and Blue, we are the chosen few,
and the Villa go marching on, on, on.
Glory glory Aston Villa
Glory glory Aston Villa
Glory glory Aston Villa
and the Villa go marching on, on, on!

BARNET

A Nine-point Christmas
(To the tune of 'White Christmas')
I'm dreaming of a nine-point Christmas
Just like the ones I used to know
Where the goalposts glistened
And children listened
To hear the Hive in full flow (in full flow)

We're On Our Way
We're on our way
We're on our way
Up the Football League, we're on our way
How do we get there, I don't know
How do we get there, I don't care
All I know is Barnet's on their way

Barnet Chant

We all follow the Barnet
Over land and sea (and Runcorn)
We'll all follow the Flash-man to the cemetery
('Land of Hope and Glory' version during the
1992–93 season when Stan Flashman led the
club to the brink of extinction)

Down the Pub the Other Night

Down the pub the other night,
People said to me they've seen the new Ian Wright,
I said to them who can that be,
They said to me its Grazioli,
Grazioli, Grazioli, Grazioli, Grazioli...
(In praise of the prolific striker)

My Old Man's A Dustman

My old man's a dustman
He wears a fireman's hat
He killed 10,000 Germans
So what d'ya think of that
One lay here, one lay there, one lay round the corner
A poor ol' soul with a bullet up his hole
was crying out for water
Water, water, water, water came at last
I don't want your water so stick it up your
Ask her round for tea; and all the family
If she don't come I'll tickle her bum with a lump of celery
Celery, celery
If she don't come I'll tickle her bum with a lump of celery

BARNSLEY

Hello Hello We Are the Barnsley boys

(To the tune of 'Hello, Hello, Who's Your Lady Friend')
Hello hello we are the Barnsley boys,
Hello hello we are the Barnsley boys,
And if you are a Wednesday fan surrender or you die,
We all follow the Barnsley...

BIRMINGHAM CITY

Birmingham Chant
(To the tune of 'Oh When the Saints')
My garden shed
Is bigger than this
My garden shed
Is bigger than this
It's got a door
And a window
My garden shed
Is bigger than this
*(Sung by City fans when visiting some of the
smaller grounds in the League)*

Don't Cry For Me Aston Villa

(To the tune of 'Don't Cry For Me Argentina')
Don't cry for me Aston Villa
The truth is I cannot stand you
All through my wild days
My mad existence
We took the Holte End
Without resistance

S**t on the Villa

S**t on the Villa
S**t on the Villa tonight
*(Based on decades of unfriendly
rivalry with Aston Villa)*

Birmingham City FC

And it's Birmingham City
Birmingham City FC
We're by far the greatest team
The world has ever seen

BLACKPOOL

We Hate Preston North End

When I was a young boy
I asked my father what would I be
Should I be Blackpool or PNE
This is what he said to me:
Wash your mouth out son
And get your father's gun
And shoot some Preston scum,
shoot some Preston scum

Ooooooooo, we hate Preston North End,
We hate Preston too
And Preston
We hate Preston North End and
Preston weeeee hate you

Barmy Army

Barmy army,
Seaside!
Barmy army,
Seaside!

Cheer Up Sean Dyche
(To the tune of 'Daydream Believer')
Cheer up, Mr Dyche
Oh what can it be
For those
Sad Burnley b**tards
And a
S**t football team

Blackpool Chant
Chim, chiminee, chim, chiminee
Chim, chim, cherou
We hate the b**tards in claret and blue
(Burnley by any chance?)

Come On, You Pool
Come on, you Pool,
Come on, you Pool,
Come on, you Pool,
Come on, you Pool

Just Can't Get Enough
(Sung to the tune of 'Just Can't Get Enough')
When I see the Blackpool, I go out of my head!
I just cant get enough, I just can't get enough,
All the things you've done to me, and all the things you've said,
I just can't get enough, I just can't get enough,
We are the Pool and we're staying up,
And we just can't seem to get enough of you

BOLTON WANDERERS

Can We Play You Every Week?
Can we play you every week?
*(Credited with being the first to sing this during the 4-1 win
at Middlesbrough in February 1996, when rooted to
the foot of the Premier League)*

Bolton Chant
Where were you when you were s***?
*(to Blackburn's new-found jump-on-the-
Jack-Walker-bandwagon fans)*

Classic Mark Fish Chant
Fiiiiiiiiiish
(Adopted South African chant for whenever
Mark Fish touches the ball)

Bolton Barmy Army
Ooooooooooooooooooohhhhhhhhhhhh
We keep chickens (Feeeesh) in our back yard
We feed 'em ('im) on Indian (African) corn
And one's a bugger for giving the other
A piggy back over the wall
O we're the barmy Bolton army na-na-na-na-na
nana, ner ner

Burnden Aces
Oh my lads you should of seen 'em runnin,
Asked them why and they replied, the Bolton boys are comin,
All the lads and lasses .... smiles upon their faces,
Walkin down the Manny road ..... to see the Burnden Aces.

Classic Mixu Paatelainen Chant
(To the tune of 'There's No Limit')
Mixu
Mixu Mixu
Mixu Mixu
Mixu Paaa-te-leinen

I'm Bolton Till I Die
I'm Bolton till I die,
I'm Bolton till I die,
I know I am,
I'm sure I am,
I'm Bolton till I die...

Classic John McGinlay Chant

We've got something you've not got
We've got something you've not got
We've got something you've not got
Super John McGinlay
Super, super John
Super, super John
Super, super John
Super John McGinlay

Bolton Wanderers FC

And it's Bolton Wanderers,
Bolton Wanderers FC,
We're by far the greatest team,
The world has ever seen...

E I E I E I O

E I E I E I O,
Up the football league we go,
When we get to Europe,
This is what we'll sing,
We are Bolton,
We are Bolton,
We're the football kings...

I Was Born Under A Wanderers scarf
(To the tune of 'I Was Born Under A Wandering Star')
I was born
Under a Wanderers scarf
I was born
Under a Wanderers scarf
Knives are made for stabbing
Guns are made to shoot
If you come in the Lever End we'll all stick in the boot
I was born under a Wanderers scarf

Oh Lancashire
Oh Lancashire, (Oh Lancashire),
Is wonderful (is wonderful)
Oh Lancashire is wonderful,
It's full of t*ts, f***y and Wanderers,
Oh Lancashire is wonderful...

Wigan Scum
Yer mum's yer dad,
Yer dad's yer mum,
Yer interbred,
You Wigan scum!
(Sung when playing bitter rivals Wigan)

Jingle Bells

Jingle bells,
Jingle bells,
Jingle all the way,
Oh what fun it is to see
Wanderers win away...

There's Only One Emile Heskey

There's only one Emile Heskey!
he used to be s**te,
but now he's alright,
walking in a Heskey wonderland.

The Queen Follows the Wanderers

The Queen follows the Wanderers
The Queen follows the Wanderers
The Queen follows the Wanderers
And hates the Blackburn scum

Classic "Is it Anelka?" Chant

(Sang to the tune 'Is It A Monster')
What's that coming over the hill, is it Anelka,
is it Anelkaaaaa?

BOURNEMOUTH

We Are the Bournemouth
We are the Bournemouth
We play at Dean Court
We live beside the seaside, but we haven't got a port
Pompey have got one, Scum have one as well
Pompey play at Fratton Park and Scummers
f***ing smell

Fratton Park is Falling Down
(To the tune of 'London Bridge Is Falling Down')
Fratton Park is falling down
Falling down, falling down
Fratton Park is falling down
Poor old Pompey

Build it up with red and black
Red and black
Red and black
Build it up with red and black
Poor old Pompey

Play Up Boscombe Town
Never let us down
Score a goal and score some more
You're the team that we adore
Win the game today
Win them all away
Play up Boscombe
Play up Boscombe
Play up Boscombe Town
(Club was known as Bournemouth
& Boscombe AFC until 1972)

Everywhere We Go
Everywhere we go *(repeat)*
People wanna know *(repeat)*
Who the f*** we are *(repeat)*
So we tell 'em *(repeat)*
We're from Bournemouth *(repeat)*
Sunny sunny Bournemouth *(repeat)*
If you can't hear us *(repeat)*
We'll sing a little louder *(repeat)*

Bournemouth Chant
I've travelled this land for many a year
Spent all my money on football and beer
Supporting the Bournemouth is why we are here
And we'll get promotion in less than a year

Bourenmouth We Love You
We all hate Brighton and Hove Albion
we hate Reading too (They're s***!)
we hate Pompey and Scummers
but Bournemouth we love you
(all together now)

Flying High, Up in the Sky
Flying high, up in the sky,
We'll keep the red flag flying high,
From Dean Court to Wembley,
We'll keep the red flag flying high.

No One's Heard Of Us
No one's heard of us,
no one's heard of us,
no one's heard of us
but we don't care

BRADFORD CITY

Bradford Chant (1)
Come on, you yellows
*(Unoriginal but, even worse, City actually play
in claret and amber shirts, not yellow)*

Bradford Chant (2)
(Clapping to the rhythm of..)
1-2
1-2-3
1-2-3-4
City!

Que Sera Sera
When I was just a little boy,
I asked my mother what should I be,
Should I be Bradford,
Should I be Leeds,
Here's what she said to me,
Wash yer mouth out son,
And go and get yer fathers gun,
And shoot the Leeds scum,
Shoot the Leeds Scum...
(Lyrics that Doris Day would not recognize)

BRIGHTON & HOVE ALBION

Brighton and Hove Albion
And it's Brighton and Hove Albion,
Brighton and Hove Albion FC,
We're by far the greatest team,
The world has ever seen...

Brighton Chant
In 1983 we went to Wembley
To play Man United and make history
Robbo was through, but he passed it to Smith
The stupid Scotch b**tard was pissed and he missed

And it's Brighton Hove Albion
Brighton Hove Albion FC
We're by far the greatest team
The world has ever seen

Good Ol' Sussex By the Sea

Good Ol' Sussex By The Sea,
Good Ol' Sussex By The Sea,
Oh We're Going Up To Win The Cup,
For Sussex By The Sea,
All Together Now...
(Repeated)

Brighton Aces

All the lads should've seen us coming,
Everyone was blue and white,
Everyone was running,
All the lads and lasses,
All with smiling faces,
Going down Old Shoreham Road,
To see the Brighton Aces...

Stick your f***ing Priestfield Up Yer A***

You can stick your f***ing Priestfield up yer a***
You can stick your f***ing Priestfield up yer a***
You can stick your f***ing Priestfield
Stick your f***ing Priestfield
Stick your f***ing Priestfield up yer a***

(Planning permission took a long time for Brighton's new stadium and exiled fans sang their disapproval at having to share Gillingham's Priestfield 40 miles away)

It's Grim Up North

Up North,
It's f***ing grim up North,
It's f**king grim up North,
Up North,
It's f***king grim up North,
It's f***king grim up North...

(A chant exclusively for away trips north of Watford)

Albion!

Albion, Albion, Albion,
Albion, Albion, Albion,
Albion, Albion, Albion,
Albion!

BRISTOL CITY

Drink Up Thee Cider
Drink up thee cider,
Drink up thee cider,
For tonight we'll merry be (merry be)
We'll go on down to Rovers,
To do the b**stards over,
And still pour cider in thee jar,

Flying High Up in the Sky
Flying high up in the sky,
We'll keep the red flag flying high,
Cider heads until we die,
We'll keep the red flag flying high...

I Am A Cider Drinker

I am a cider drinker,
I drinks it all of the day,
I am a cider drinker,
It sooths all me troubles away,
Oorr, oorr, oorroorrayy...

Fight Fight

Fight fight wherever you may be,
We are the boys from the West Country,
And we don't like you all, whomever you may be,
'Cos we are the boys from the West Country...

BRISTOL ROVERS

Irene, Goodnight Irene

We're loyal supporters, we're faithful and true
We always follow, the boys in blue (and white)
We all made a promise, that we'll never part
So Goodnight Irene, I'll see you in my dreams
('Irene, Goodnight Irene' was regularly played at Rovers'
former home Eastville from the 1950s. The bit that goes:
'Sometimes I have a great notion, to jump in the river and
drown', would have appealed to fans after watching their team
lose, as the river ran alongside the ground)

Who's That Team

Who's that team they call the City
Who's that team that never scores
And they play in red and white
And they're a load of s**te
And their manager's mother is a whore
(Rovers' supporters vent their wrath at the city's
other major team Bristol City)

Come On You Gas

Come on, you Gas
Come on, you Gas
Come on, you Gas
Come on, you Gas

We're Gas

We're Gas and we're going up
We're Gas and we're going up
We're Gas and we're going up
(Eastville was next to a gas works. Fans said that
when the heads of the gasometers were rising, the smell
overcame the opposition and helped Rovers win,
hence the name Gasheads)

You've Got Me Singing the Blues!

I never felt more like singing the Blues
Than when Rovers win, and City lose
Oooo Rovers
You've got me singing the Blues!
We hate Joe Jordan, and all of the reds
The only good City fan is one that's dead
Oooo Rovers
You've got me singing the Blues

We Are Rovers

We are Rovers,
super Rovers,
we are Rovers,
from the Mem,
we are Rovers,
we are Rovers,
super Rovers,
from the Mem,
we are Rovers,
super Rovers,
we are Rovers,
from the Mem!

Red, Red Robin

When the red, red, robin goes bob, bob
bobbin' along
Shoot the b**tard
Shoot the b**tard
Shoot, shoot, shoot the b**tard

He's Only A Poor Little Robin

He's only a poor little Robin
His wings are all tattered and torn
He made me feel sick
So I hit him with a brick
And now he don't sing any more!

It's a Massacre

Oooh Aaar,
it's a massacre,
Oooh Aaar,
it's a massacre,
Oooh Aaar,
it's a massacre,
Oooh Aaar,
it's a massacre!

All Hate Bristol City

All hate Bristol City,
All hate Bristol City,
All hate Bristol City clap your hands...

If you really F***in hate 'em,
Really F***in hate 'em,
Really F***in hate 'em clap your hands!!
(For the attention of arch rivals Bristol City)

Aston Gate is Full Of S***

Oh Ashton Gate (oh Ashton Gate)
Is full of s*** (is full of s***)
Oh Ashton Gate is full of s***
Full of s***, s*** and more s***
Oh Ashton Gate is full of s***

Oh, Rovers Rovers

Oh, Rovers Rovers,
What ever will be will be,
We really have to say,
We secretly love City.

Bristol Rovers!

Na na na na, na na na na,
whhhhheeeyyyyyyyyyyy,
Bristol Rovers!

Na na na na, na na na na,
whhhhheeeyyyyyyyyyy,
Bristol Rovers!

West Country, La La La

West Country, la la la
West Country, la la la
West Country, la la la
West Country, la la la

One Team In Bristol

One team in Bristol,
there's only one team in Bristol,
one team in Bristol,
there's only one team in Bristol!

BURNLEY

One Man and his Dog
One man went to s***
Went to s*** on Ewood
One man and his dog (Spot)
Went to s*** on Ewood

Two men went to s***
Went to s*** on Ewood
Two men and their dog (Spot)
Went to s*** on Ewood
(Repeat up to ten)

He's F***ed Off Home
He's f***ed off home
He's f***ed off home
He's f***ed off
Shearer's f***ed off home
(After the striker quit Blackburn for Newcastle)

CAMBRIDGE UNITED

Cheer Up Barry Fry
(To the tune of 'Daydream Believer')
Cheer up Barry Fry
Oh what can it mean
To a fat 'Boro b**tard
And a s*** football team
*(The boss of near neighbour Peterborough United
takes some flak)*

Cambridge Chant
1-2 *(clap, clap)*
1-2-3 *(clap, clap, clap)*
1-2-3-4 *(clap, clap, clap, clap)*
5-1 *(clap, clap)*
(Reference to an ancient 5–1 win at Peterborough)

CARDIFF CITY

It's Full of S***
It's full of s***, it's full of s***
It's full of ...
England's full of s***

In the Swansea Slums
In the Swansea slums,
They look in the dustbins for something to eat,
They find a dead rat and they think it's a treat,
In the Swansea slums...
(For the attention of bitter rivals Swansea)

We're Cardiff City
We're top of the league,
We're top of the league,
We're Cardiff City,
We're top of the league...

Cardiff Chant
1-0 to the sheep shaggers

CARLISLE UNITED

We're Going Up
We're going up, we're going up
We're going, Carlisle's going up

If You're Proud
If you're proud to be a Cumbrian, clap your hands!

We'd Rather Shag a Sheep
We'd rather shag a sheep than a Mackem
We'd rather shag a sheep than a Mackem
Oh we'd rather shag a sheep
Rather shag a sheep
Rather shag a sheep than a Mackem
*(Carlisle fans from the west coast seem to have something
against Sunderland on the east coast)*

Carlisle Chant
(To the tune of the 'Can Can')
1-0 to the sheep shaggers

We Are Carlisle

We are Carlisle, super Carlisle, we are Carlisle,
from the north
No one likes us, no one likes us, but we are Carlisle
and we don't care
'Cos we are Carlisle, super Carlisle, we are Carlisle,
from the north

We Are Cumbrians

Cumbrians, we are Cumbrians
Cumbrians, we are Cumbrians
Cumbrians, we are Cumbrians
Oh yes, we are Cumbrians

CHARLTON ATHLETIC

Stand Up ... Sit Down
Stand up, if you hate Millwall
Sit down, if you hate Palace

Valley Floyd Road
(To the tune of 'Mull of Kintyre')
Valley Floyd Road
Oh mist rolling in from the Thames
My desire is always to be here
Oh Valley Floyd Road

We Are Charlton
We are Charlton,
We are Charlton,
Super Charlton,
Over here.

South London La-La-La
South London la-la-la,
South London la-la-la,
South London la-la-la,
South London la-la-la, la-la-la

CHELSEA

The Blue Flag

Forever and ever we'll follow our team
For we are the Chelsea and we are supreme
We'll never be mastered by no northern b**tards
And we'll keep the Blue Flag flying high
Flying high, up in the sky
We'll keep the Blue Flag flying high
From Stamford Bridge to Wemb(er)ley
We'll keep the Blue Flag flying high

One Man Went To Mow

One man went to mow
Went to mow a meadow
One man and his dog (Spot)
Went to mow a meadow

Two men went to mow
Went to mow a meadow
Two men and their dog (Spot)
Went to mow a meadow
(Repeat up to ten men...)

When It's Snowing
Sing when it's snowing
You only sing when it's snowing
Sing when it's snowing
*(Home leg of the 1997–98 European Cup-Winners' Cup tie
with Tromsø of Norway, following a first leg played
during a snowstorm)*

Administration
La la la la la
Administration la la la la la la
Administration la la la la la la
(Sung at Elland Road to the fans of hard-up Leeds)

Who's That Team They Call the Chelsea?

Who's that team they call the Chelsea?
Who's that team we all adore?
We're the boys in blue and white
And we fight with all' our might
And we're out to show the world the way to score

Bring on Tottenham or the Arsenal
Bring on Scousers by the score
Barcelona, Real Madrid, Tottenham are a load of s**ts
And we're out to show the world the way to score

Keep Your Wife From John Terry

Chelsea,
wherever you may be,
keep your wife from
John Terry

*(To the tune of 'Lord of the Dance', Chelsea fans
salute their Captain after his alleged affair with
former team-mate Wayne Bridge's ex-girlfriend)*

We All F***ing Hate Leeds

Leeds, Leeds and Leeds and Leeds
And Leeds
Leeds, and Leeds and Leeds
And Leeds, and Leeds and Leeds and Leeds
We all f***ing hate Leeds

We Are the famous CFC

Carefree wherever you may be
We are the famous CFC
And we don't give a f*** whoever you may be
'Cos we are the famous CFC

Classic Frank Leboeuf Chant (1)

He's here, he's there
He's every f***ing where
Frank Leboeuf, Frank Leboeuf

Classic Frank Leboeuf Chant (2)

He's here, he's there
We're not allowed to swear
Frank Leboeuf, Frank Leboeuf
(Following a request from the player)

Classic Vialli Chant

He came from Italy
To play for Che-el-sea
Vialli, o-o-o-o-oh Vialli

CHESTER FC

Chester Chant

Can you hear the Wrexham sing?
No-oh, no-oh
Can you hear the Wrexham sing?
No-oh, no-oh
Can you hear the Wrexham sing?
I can't hear a f***ing thing
No-oh, no-oh no-oh

Those Were the Days

If you were born in Wales
You've probably heard the tales
Of Chester fans and what we do to you
We go to Wrexham town
And burn the stand right down
And build it up in royal blue and white
Die! Die! Die! Die Wrexham!

We're A Grand Old Team To Play For

And we're a grand old team to play for,
And we're a grand old team to support,
And if you know your history,
It's enough to make your heart go,
woooooooooohh...

CHESTERFIELD

Burn the Lot

Build a bonfire, build a bonfire
Put United on the top
Put the Wednesday in the middle
And burn the f***ing lot
(A little ditty dedicated to the neighbouring Sheffield clubs)

Chesterfield Chant

Skies are blue, clouds are white
God must be a Spireite
Der-der-der-der
Der-der-der
Der-der

Chim-Chiminee

Chim, chiminee, chim, chiminee
Chim, chim, cherou
We hate the scabbing b**tards
In yellow and blue
(For the fans at Mansfield Town)

Elleray

Elleray, Elleray,
We're the famous Chesterfield
And we were robbed by Elleray
*(After 1996–97 run to the FA Cup semi-finals
was halted by the aforementioned referee)*

COVENTRY CITY

Go For It, City
Go for it
Go for it, City
Sky Blues shooting to win

Mickey Quinn
He's fat, he's round
He scores on every ground
Mickey Quinn, Mickey Quinn

CREWE ALEXANDRA

Blue Moon
Blue Moon, you saw me standing alone,
Without a dream in my heart,
Without a love of my own...
*(Crewe are generally credited with being the first fans to sing
this, and they sing it in its entirety, though it has since been
adopted by Man City)*

Ing-er-land
Ing-er-land, Ing-er-land, Ing-er-land
(Reserved for Wrexham)

Crewe Chant
And it's Crewe Alexandra
Crewe Alexandra FC
They're by far the greatest team
The world has ever seen

The Clayhead Scum

When I was just a little boy,
I asked my mother
what will it be
Will it be Vale? Will it be Stoke?
Here's what
she said to me
Wash your mouth out son, and get your father's gun
And shoot the Clayhead scum
And shoot the Clayhead scum

Sheep Shaggers

Sheep, sheep, sheep shaggers
(also reserved for Wrexham)

CRYSTAL PALACE

Eagles
Eagles, Eagles, Eagles

We Are Palace
We are Palace, super Palace
We are Palace from Selhurst

Glad All Over
Glad All Over
*(The Dave Clark Five Number 1 hit of 1964 is sung
as the teams run out at the start of the match)*

DARLINGTON 1883

Sack the Board
Sack the board, sack the board, sack the board
(A regular chant given Darlington's chequered history)

You're So Crap
You're so crap you're worse than Hartlepool

I'm Henry the VIII
I'm Henry the VIII I am
I got married to the widow next door
She's been married seven times before
And everyone was a Henry
Never a Willy or a Sam

DERBY COUNTY

We Are Derby
We are Derby,
We are Derby,
Super Derby,
Super Rams.

Could Be Worse
Could be worse,
We could be Leeds,
Could be worse,
We could be Leeds...

EVERTON

Ever-ton
Ever-ton, Ever-ton, Ever-ton
Ever-ton, Ever-ton, Ever-ton
Ever-ton, Ever-ton, Ever-ton
Ever-ton, Ever-ton

You Are My Everton
You are my Everton, my only Everton
You make me happy when skies are grey
You'll never know just how much I love you
So please never take my Everton away

Leighton Baines
(To the tune of Carly Simon's 'You're So Vain')
Leighton Baines,
you probably think this song is about you

No Woman, No Kai
No woman, no Kai
(Fans who once adored him had this chant for former Evertonian Wayne Rooney when it was alleged the Man Utd player was paying for sex while his wife was pregnant with son Kai. Sung to the tune of Bob Marley's 'No Woman, No Cry')

It's A Grand Old Team To Play For

It's a grand old team to play for
It's a grand old team to support
And if you know the history
It's enough to make your heart go
Oooooooooooo

We don't care what the Red s**te say
What the f*** do we care
We only know there's going to be a show
And the Everton boys will be there

All You Need is Moyes

All you need is Moyes, da da da da da
All you need is Moyes, da da da da da
All you need is Moyes,
Moyes is all you need
(But the affection for manager David Moyes changed
when he left for Man Utd)

EXETER CITY

We'll Score Again
(To the tune of 'We'll meet again')
We'll score again
Don't know where
Don't know when
But I know we'll score again some sunny day

Keep smiling through
Just like we always do
'Cos you know we'll score again
Some sunny day

Will you please say hello
To the folks that I know
And tell them I won't be long
You'll be happy to know
While we wait for a goal
We'll keep singing this song

We'll score again
Don't know where
Don't know when
But I know we'll score again some sunny day

Green and White Cop
(To the tune of 'Yellow Submarine')
We all p*** in a green and white kop
In a green and white kop
A green and white kop
A green and white kop

I Comes From the West Country
I can't read and I can't write
But that don't really matter
'Cos I comes from the West Country
And I can drive a tractor

FULHAM

Can't Live
I Can't live
If livin' is without you
*(The 1970s live on at Craven Cottage where
this old hit is sung on a regular basis)*

Dicks Out
Dicks out
*(A double entendre reminder for under-fire boss Alan Dicks to
make the ultimate sacrifice during the early 90s)*

That's Zamora
When you're sat in row Z,
and the ball hits your head
that's Zamora, that's Zamora
*(Fulham supporters on former goal-shy striker Bobby Zamora,
sung to the tune of Dean Martin's 'That's Amore')*

Came For the Ball Boys
Came for the ball boys
You only came for the ball boys
(Chanted at members of the away support)

You'll Never Play Us Again
You'll never play us again
You'll never play us again
You'll never play us again
*(When Brentford were heading for the basement
division and it seemed as if Fulham might
be going up in the 1997–98 season)*

HARTLEPOOL UNITED

Hark Now Hear
Hark now hear, the 'Pool sing
The Dario ran away
Where were you on Boxing Day?
The fighting started, you ran away

HUDDERSFIELD TOWN

Smile A While

There's a team that's dear to its followers
Their colours are bright blue and white
They're a team of reknown, they're the talk of the town
And the game of football is their delight

All the while upon the field of play
Thousands gladly cheered them on their way
Often you could hear them say,
"Who can beat the Town today?"

Then the bells shall ring so merrily
Every goal shall be a memory
So town play up and bring the Cup
Back to Huddersfield

Those Were the Days

Those were the days my friend
I thought they'd never end
We won the League three times in a row
We won the FA Cup
And now we're going up
We are the Town
Oh yes, we are the Town

HULL CITY

Common Dolan

(To the tune of 'Common People' by Pulp)
He came from Rochdale with a lack of knowledge
He studied management at Bradford College
That's where I *(pause)*, caught his eye
He told me that he was a manager
I said:"In that case you'd better come and manage us"
He said:"Fine"
And then, in three seasons' time
He said:"I want to take you to the Vauxhall Conference
I want to do whatever Halifax do
I want to sign lots of crap old players
I want to watch this club slide out of view
And hoof, and hoof and hoof
Because
There's nothing left to dooooooooooo"

Living the Dream

Sing loud, sing strong, Hull City AFC
they fight for us, they try for us, the bravest there can be
we'll meet again, but while we are apart
you ask me where these memories live,

I've known it from the start
you ask me where these memories live,
they live within my heart

Sing loud, sing strong, remember Boothferry Park
from North Stand Clock to Bunker's Hill,

The Tigers made their mark
we'll meet again, but while we are apart
you ask me where these memories live,

I've known it from the start
you ask me where these memories live,
they live within my heart

Sing loud, sing strong, the FC is our friend
new history seen, let's live the dream, supporters to the end
we'll meet again, but while we are apart
you ask me where these memories live,

I've known it from the start
you ask me where these memories live,
they live within my heart

Hull City now and ever more, we've known it from the start
stand up and hear the Tigers roar
they live within my heart.

A Black and Amber Team

(To the tune of 'Yellow Submarine')

In the town, where I was born
There's a teeeeeeaaaaaaaam
Called Hull City
And we make, the pilgrimage
On a Saturday, to Boothferry
We all follow a black and amber team
A black and amber team
Who sometimes play in green

IPSWICH TOWN

The Blues

I never felt more like singing the Blues
When Ipswich win and Norwich lose
Oh Ipswich, you got me singing the Blues

I never felt more like singing the Blues
When Ipswich hit five, that's all right
Oh Ipswich, you got me singing the Blues

The moon and stars always shine
The super blues are fine, fine, fine
There's nothing else I'd rather do
Then spend my time with the super blues
(Repeat second verse, then third verse and finally first verse)

The Pride of Anglia

Who are the s**ts of Anglia?
Narrrrwich, Narrrrwich
Who are the pride of Anglia?
Ipswich, Ipswich
We're the pride of Anglia
Ipswich is our name

He's Only A Poor Little Budgie

He's only a poor little budgie
His shirt is all tattered and torn
He started to sing
So we filled the **** in
And now he don't sing anymore

LEEDS UNITED

We Are Leeds
We are Leeds, we are Leeds
We are Leeds
We are Leeds, we are Leeds
We are Lee-eeds
We are Leeds, we are Leeds
We are Leeds
We are Lee-eeds
We are Leeds!

Marching On Together
Here we go with Leeds United, we're going
to give the boys a hand
Stand up and sing for Leeds United, they're the
greatest in the land

Everyday we're all going to say we love you
Leeds, Leeds, Leeds
Everywhere we're all going to be there, we love you
Leeds; Leeds, Leeds
We're gonna see you win
'Cos we're so proud
We shout it out loud
We love you Leeds, Leeds, Leeds

When I Was Just

When I was just a little boy
I asked my mother, "What should I be?"
"Should I be Chelsea?
Should I be Leeds?"
Here's what she said to me:
"Wash your mouth out son
And go get your father's gun
And shoot the Chelsea scum
Shoot the Chelsea scum'
We hate Chelsea
We hate Chelsea

We Had Joy

We had joy, we had fun
We had Man U on the run
But the joy didn't last
'Cos the b**tards ran too fast!

Hark now Hear

Hark now hear, United sing
The Man U ran away
And there will be a massacre
Upon this Saturday

Who Do You Think You Are Kidding Mr Ferguson
(To the tune of 'Dad's Army theme')

Who do you think you are kidding, Mr Ferguson
If you think you'll win the League
We are the boys who will stop your little game
We are the boys who will win the League again

When He Just Buys the Club
When he just buys the club
He goes straight to the pub,
That's Cellino

Marching On Together
We've been through it all together,
And we've had our ups and downs (ups and downs)
We're gonna stay with you forever,
At least until the world stops going round

We Are Sailing

We are sailing,
We are sailing,
Up the Table,
Up the league,
No more Wednesday, f**k off Wednesday,
We are sailing,
We are Leeds

No Income Tax, No VAT

(To the Only Fools and Horses theme tune, 'Hooky Street')
No income tax, no VAT
Hiding yachts in Italy
Blue and white
No longer poor
We're Leeds United
Forever more

LEICESTER CITY

Are You Watching?
Are you watching
Are you watching
Are you watching Mark McGhee?

All Things Bright and Beautiful
All things bright and beautiful
All creatures great and small
Leicester rule the midlands
And Forest rule f**k all
(Having a pop at local rivals Nottingham Forest)

When You're Tired and Weary
When you're tired and weary
Your heart will skip a beat
You'll get your f*cking head kicked in
As you walk down Filbert Street
You'll walk into the Spion Kop
You'll hear a mighty roar
F*ck off you Forest B*st*rds
We are the Leicester Boys.

LINCOLN CITY

S**t Refs
S**t refs and we're sick of 'em
(After a run of games poorly refereed)

We Smell Fish
We smell fish, we smell fish
(Turning noses up at rivals Grimsby Town)

LIVERPOOL

The Reds Are Coming Up the Hill
The Reds are coming up the hill, boys
The Reds are coming up the hill, boys
They all laugh at us, they all laugh at us
They all say our days are numbered
Born to be a Scouse
Victorious are we
You wanna win the Cup, then you'd better hurry up
'Cos Liverpool FC ...
Glorious, victorious, etc ...

Here's A Song About a Football Team
Here's a song about a football team
The greatest team you've ever seen
A team that play total football
They've won the league,
Europe and all

We All Live In a Red and White Kop
(To the tune of 'Yellow Submarine')
We all live in a red and white Kop
A red and white Kop
A red and white Kop
We all live in a red and white Kop
A red and white Kop
A red and white Kop
A red and white Kop
A red and white Kop

Robbie Keane
He's fast, he's red, he talks like Father Ted.
(Fans' salute to striker Robbie Keane)

Now If You Go Down Goodison Way
Now if you go down Goodison Way
Hard luck stories you hear each day
There's not a trophy to be seen
'Cos Liverpool have swept them clean

Red River Valley

Let me tell you the story of a poor boy
Who was sent far away from his home
To fight for his king and his country
And all the old folks back home
They put him in a second division
Sent him off to a far foreign field
Where the flies swarm around in their thousands
And there's nothing to see but the sand
Now the battle it started next morning
Under the Arabian sun
I remember the poor Scouser Tommy
Who was shot by an old Nazi gun
He lay on the battlefield dying
With the blood rushing out of his head
As he lay on the battlefield dying, dying, dying
These were the last words he said,
"Oh, I'm a Liverpudlian and I come from the Spion Kop
I like to sing, I like to shout
And get thrown out quite alot
We support a team that's dressed in red
It's a team that you all know
It's a team we call Li-ver-pool
And to glory we will go!"

We Won the League

We won the League, we won the League Cup
And we've been to Europe, too
We played the Toffees for a laugh
And left them feeling blue
1-0, 2-0, 3-0, 4-0, 5-0

On A Saturday Afternoon

On a Saturday afternoon
We support a team called Liverpool
And we sing until we drop
On the famous Spion Kop

You'll Never Walk Alone

Walk on, walk on, with hope in your heart
And you'll never walk alone
You'll never walk alone
(Anfield anthem, adopted in th 1960s)

MANCHESTER CITY

Are You Watching?
Are you watching?
Are you watching?
Are you watching Macclesfield
*(Fans' ironic reaction to City's relegation in the 1997–98
season, which meant future derby meetings with their new
Cheshire-based Macclesfield instead of Man Utd)*

Feed the Goat and He Will Score
Feed the Goat and he will score
Feed the Goat and he will score
(Striker Shaun Goater was a favourite with Blues' fans)

We Never Win

We never win at home and we never win away
We lost last week and we're losing today
We don't give a f***
'Cos we're all pissed up
MCFC OK

Niall Quinn's Disco Pants

Niall Quinn's disco pants are the best
They come up from his a*** to his chest
They're better than Adam and the Ants
Niall Quinn's disco pants
*(Adopted after the former City striker
was seen out on the town one night)*

We're Not Really Here

We're not really here, we're not really here
Like the friends of the Invisible Man
We're not really here
*(Inspired by City fans on tour in Ireland who trashed the bar of
the Metropole Hotel in Cork, then sang this to the police officer
sent to deal with the situation in the belief there was
no proof as to which of them were responsible)*

Alan Ball

(To the tune of Oasis's 'Wonderwall')
And all the runs that Kinky makes are winding
And all the goals that City score are blinding
There are many times that we would like to score again
But we don't know how
'Cos maybe
You're gonna be the one that saves me
And after all
You're my Alan Ball

We've Lost That Terry Phelan

(To the tune of 'We've Lost That Lovin' Feelin')
We've lost that Terry Phelan
Woah that Terry Phelan
We've lost that Terry Phelan
Now he's gone, gone, gone,
Wooooah

That Coat's from Matalan

That coat's from Matalan!
That coat's from Matalan!
*(Mocking Chelsea's Jose Mourinho who often wore an
expensive coat on the touchline)*

They Say That Old Trafford's A Wonderful Place

They say that Old Trafford's a wonderful place
but the team that plays there are a f***ing disgrace
with half-backs and full-backs and forwards too
their hands down their pants cos they've f*** all to do
the Stretford End sing and the Stretford End shout
but the songs that they sing they know f*** all about
and we all agree where United should be
shovelling S*** on the Isle of Capri
Oh Capri
Oh Capri

Pellegrini

Pellegrin-i,
Pellegrin-i,
The best manager,
We've ever seen-i,
He comes from abroad,
And now we're never bored,
'cos we score ten goals each game

Pellegrin-i,
Pellegrin-i,
his big puffy coat,
Is the best we've ever seen-i,
He's got us to the top,
Now we're too good to stop,
Man United where are you?

City Chant (1)
Oh Man City
The only English team to win the championship
(They claim no other team has won the League title with 11 Englishmen)

City Chant (2)
Oh Man City
The only football team to come from Manchester
(A dig at United's countrywide support)

Sha La La La La La La City
Sha la la la la la la City
Sha la la la la la la City
Sha la la la la la la City
We are the kings of England

City, City, City

In 1963 when we fell to Division Two
The Stretford End cried out aloud
"It's the end for you, Sky Blue"
Joe Mercer came
We played the game
We went to Rotherham
And won 1-0
And we were back into Division One
We've won the League, we've won the League Cup
We've been to Europe too
And when we win the League again
We'll sing this song to you
City, City, City, City, City

No More Fergie

(To the tune of "There's No Limit")
No no no no no no no no no no more Fergie
no no no no no no no no no no more Fergie
no no Fergie
he's given up the fight
his watch has packed up
and his hip isn't right
(Sung for Manchester United)

MANCHESTER UNITED

Keano's Magic

Oh, Keano's f***ing magic
He wears a magic hat
And when he saw Old Trafford
He said, "I fancy that"
He didn't sign for Arsenal
Or Blackburn 'cos they're s**te
He signed for Man United
'Cos they're f***ing dynamite

You Are My Solskjaer
(To the tune of 'You Are My Sunshine')

You are my Solskjaer
My Ole Solskjaer
You make me happy
When skies are grey
And Alan Shearer
Was f***ing dearer
So please don't take
My Solskjaer, away

Classic Paul Scholes Chant
(To the tune of 'Kumbayah')
He scores goals m'lord, he scores goals
He scores goals m'lord, he scores goals
He scores goals m'lord, he scores goals
Paul Scholes, he scores goals

Classic Ryan Giggs Chant
(To the tune of the 'Robin Hood theme')
Ryan Giggs, Ryan Giggs
Running down the wing
Ryan Giggs, Ryan Giggs
Running down the wing
Feared by the Blues
Loved by the Reds
Ryan Giggs, Ryan Giggs, Ryan Giggs

Your Teeth Are Offside
Your teeth are offside,
your teeth are offside,
Luis Suárez, your teeth are offside.
*(Liverpool forward Luis Suárez's
large gnashers get some stick)*

Drink, Drink
(To the tune of 'Lord of the Dance')
Drink, drink wherever you may be
We are the drunk and disorderly
And we don't give a s***, and we don't give a f***
We're going home with the European Cup!

Poor Little Scouser
He's only a poor little Scouser
His face is all battered and torn
He made me feel sick
So I hit him with a brick
And now he don't sing anymore

Classic Teddy Sheringham Chant
Oh Teddy Teddy
Teddy Teddy Teddy Teddy Sheringham

Aye-aye Yippie
(To the tune of 'She'll Be Coming Round The Mountain)
Singing aye-aye yippee yippee-aye
Singing aye-aye yippee yippee-aye
Singing aye-aye yippee yippee-aye
Aye-aye yippee yippee-aye
If you all hate Scousers, clap your hands
If you all hate Scousers, clap your hands
If you all hate Scousers, all hate Scousers
All hate Scousers, clap your hands!

Nemanja, Woah-oh
Nemanja, woah-oh
Nemanja, woah-oh
He comes from Serbia,
He'll f***ing murder ya

Rio Ferdinand
(To the tune of 'Rio' by Duran Duran)
His name is Rio
and he watches from the stand
*(Rio Ferdinand faced this chant when banned
for missing a drugs test)*

In Your Liverpool Slums

In your Liverpool slums
You look in the dustbin for something to eat
You find a dead rat and you think it's a treat
In your Liverpool slums

In your Liverpool slums
In your Liverpool slums
You speak in an accent exceedingly rare
You wear a pink tracksuit and have curly hair
In your Liverpool slums

In your Liverpool slums
In your Liverpool slums
Your mum's on the game and your dad's in the nick
You can't get a job 'cos you're too f***ing thick
In your Liverpool slums

We're the Best Behaved Supporters In the Land

We're the best behaved supporters in the land
We're the best behaved supporters in the land
We're the best behaved supporters
Best behaved supporters
Best behaved supporters in the land (when we win!)

We're a right bunch of b**tards when we lose
We're a right bunch of b**tards when we lose
We're a right bunch of b**tards
Right bunch of b**tards
Right bunch of b**tards when we lose

Rooney Got a Touch Down

Rooney got a touch down,
Rooney got a touch down, na na na,
Rooney got a touch down,
Rooney got a touch down na na na
(Sung American style when Rooney scores)

If I Had the Wings of a Sparrow

If I had the wings of a sparrow
If I had the a*** of a crow
I'd fly over Maine Road tomorrow
And s*** on the b**tards below, below
S**t on, s*** on
S**t on the b**tards below, below
S**t on, s*** on
S**t on the b**tards below

We'll Never Die

United's flag is deepest red
It shrouded all our Munich dead
Before their limbs grew stiff and cold
Their heart's blood dyed its ev'ry fold
Then raise United's banner high
Beneath its shade we'll live and die
So keep the faith and never fear

We'll keep the Red Flag flying here
We'll never die, we'll never die
We'll never die, we'll never die
We'll keep the Red flag flying high
'Cos Man United will never die

MIDDLESBROUGH

Cock of the North
We are the 'Boro, the Cock of the North
We all hate Newcastle, and Sunderland of course
We all drink whisky and Newcastle Brown
The 'Boro boys are in town
Na na na ... we are the 'Boro

We Shall Overcome
We shall overcome some day
Deep in my heart I do believe
We shall overcome some day

We Are the 'Boro boys
'Ello, 'ello, we are the 'Boro boys
'Ello, 'ello, we are the 'Boro boys
We're the Ayresome Angels
and we never miss a match
We all follow the 'Boro
(A survivor despite the move from
Ayresome Park to the Riverside stadium)

Who's That Team

All the Geordies went to Rome to see the Pope
All the Geordies went to Rome to see the Pope
And this is what he said:
"Who's that team they call the 'Boro?
Who's that team we all adore?
Oh we play in red and white
And we're f***ing dynamite
And we'll support the 'Boro ever more"

If I Had the Wings of an Eagle

If I had the wings of an eagle
and I had the a*** of a crow.
I'd fly over Sunderland tomorrow
and s*** on the a***holes below.
(Sung for the Sunderland masses)

MILLWALL

No One Likes Us
No one likes us,
No one likes us
No one likes us
We don't care
We are Millwall
Super Millwall
We are Millwall
From The Den

Millwall Chant
Let 'em come, let 'em come let 'em come
Let 'em all come down to The Den
Let 'em come, let 'em come, let 'em come
We'll only have to beat them again
It's the best team in London
The best team of all
Everybody knows us
We are called Millwall

We Hate Tuesday
We hate Tuesday, hate Tuesday
*(Millwall fans in response to Sheffield United's
chant of "We hate (Sheffield) Wednesday")*

NEWCASTLE UNITED

Black and White Army

Toon, Toon,
Black and white army,
Toon, Toon,
Black and white army,
Toon, Toon,
Black and white army,
Toon, Toon,
Black and white army,
Toon, Toon,
Black and white army.

Alan Shearer

When Alan's runnin' down the wing,
Shearer, Shearer
When Alan's runnin' down the wing,
Shearer, Shearer
When Alan's runnin' down the wing
Newcastle United begin to sing
We all know he's goin' to score a f***in' goal

Drink, Drink

(To the tune of 'Lord Of The Dance')
Drink, drink, wherever we may be
We are the drunk and disorderly
And we will drink wherever we may be
For we are the drunk and disorderly

I was drunk last night
I was drunk the night before
And I'm gonna get drunk like I've never been drunk before
'Cos when we're drunk we're as happy as can be
For we are the drunk and disorderly

When I Go A-wandering

When I go a-wandering
Along the cliffs of Dover
If I see a mackem c***
I'll push the b**tard over

Philippe Albert
(To the tune of 'Rupert the Bear')
Philippe, Philippe Albert
Everyone knows his name

Toon Toon Toon
(To the tune of the Outhere Brothers, 'Boom Boom')
Toon, Toon, Toon, everybody say wheyaye (wheyaye)

Fat Eddie Murphy
Fat Eddie Murphy, you're just a fat Eddie Murphy.
(Heckling Chelsea striker Jimmy Floyd Hasselbaink)

Blaydon Races
I went to Blaydon Races
'Twas on the 9th of June
Eighteen Hundred and Sixty Two
On a Summer's Afternoon
We took the bus from Balmbras
And she was heavy laden
Away we went along Collingwood Street
That's on the Road to Blaydon

Sad Mackem B**tard

(to the tune of 'Daydream Believer')
Cheer up Peter Reid
Oh what can it mean
To a sad Mackem b**tard
And a s*** football team

A Monkey's Head

(To the tune of 'Yellow Submarine')
In the land where I was born
Lives a man with a monkey's head
And he went to Sunderland
· And his name is Peter Reid
Altogether now
Peter Reid's got a f***in' monkey's head
A f***in' monkey's head
A f***in' monkey's head
A f***in' monkey's head
A f***in' monkey's head
Peter Reid's got a f***in' monkey's head

Mackems On A string

(To the tune of 'My Ding-a-Ling')

When I was a little bitty boy
My grandmother bought me a cute little toy
Two Sunderland fans, hanging on a string
She told me to kick their f***ing heads in

Mackems on a string
Mackems on a string
She told me to kick their f***ing heads in
Mackems on a string
Mackems on a string
She told me to kick their f***ing heads in

Geordie Boys, Take the P***

Geordie boys, take the p***
Geordie boys, take the p***
Geordie boys, take the p***
Geordie boys, take the p***

Who's That Team

Who's that team we call United?/
Who's that team we all adore?/
Oh, we play in black and white
And we all know how to fight
We'll support you ever more

We Are the Geordies

We are the Geordies, the Geordie boot boys,
For we are mental, we are mad,
We're the loudest football supporters,
the world has ever had ...

NORWICH CITY

On the Ball
On the ball City
Never mind the danger
Kick it off
Throw it in
Have a little scrimmage
Splendid rush
Bravo win or die
On the ball City
Never mind the danger

Iwan Roberts
Iwan, Iwan, Iwan
(Ironic attempt at encouraging Iwan Roberts)

Are You Watching?
Are you watching?
Are you watching?
Are you watching, Ipswich scum?
Are you watching, Ipswich scum?
*(A message to local rivals Ipswich when
the Canaries are winning)*

We've Come For Our Scarves
We've come for our scarves,
We've come for our scarves,
We're Norwich City,
We've come for our scarves

NOTTINGHAM FOREST

City Ground
(To the tune of 'Mull of Kintyre')
Far have we travelled
And much have we seen
Goodison, Anfield are places we've been
Maine Road, Old Trafford still echo to the sounds
Of the boys in the Red shirts from City Ground
City Ground
Oh mist rolling in from the Trent
My desire is always to be there
On City Ground

Sheep Shaggers
Sheep, sheep, sheep shaggers
Baaaaaaaaaaaaaaa!!
*(Well, if Derby will go and call themselves
the Rams, they can't expect much better)*

Spirit in the Sky
Going on up to the spirit in the sky,
it's where I'm gonna go when I die,
when I die and they put me in the rough,
I'm gonna go on the p*** with Brian Clough.

Stevie Stone

Stevie Stone, Stevie Stone
Stevie, Stevie Stone
He's got no hair, but we don't care
Stevie, Stevie Stone
(Special tribute to midfielder Steve Stone)

We Hate Derby (1)

We hate Derby and we hate Derby
We hate Derby and we hate Derby
We are the Derby Haters

Poetry in Motion

Poetry in motion tra la la la la
Poetry in motion tra la la la la la
Poetry in motion tra la la la la
We're the best football team in the land, yes we are
We are Nottingham tra la la la la
We are Nottingham tr la la la la la
We are Nottingham tra la la la la
We're the best football team in the land, yes, we are

We Hate Derby (2)
Away in a manger
No crib for a bed
The little lord Jesus
Woke up and he said ...
We hate Derby and we hate Derby
We hate Derby and we hate Derby
We are the Derby
Haters

Where's Your Caravan?
(To the tune of 'Where's Your Mama Gone?')
Where's your caravan, where's your caravan?
Where's your caravan, where's your caravan?
(Usually aimed at opposing players of scruffy" appearance.)

Hello, Hello

(To the tune of 'Marching through Georgia')

Hello, hello, we are the Trent End boys
Hello, hello, you'll know us by our noise
We are the best team in the land
That no one can deny
We all follow the Forest

We Love You Forest, We Do

We love you Forest, we do
We love you Forest, we do
We love you Forest, we do
Oh Forest we love you!

You've Come For Our Bins!

You've come for our bins!
You've come for our biiiiiins!
You bin-dipping b**tards!
You've come for our bins!

(For the fans at Leicester City)

We Rule Supreme
Forever and ever,
We'll follow our team,
We're Nottingham Forest.
We rule supreme!
We'll never be mastered,
By you Leicester b**tards!
We'll keep the red flag, flying high!
(For the ears of Leicester FC fans)

When I Was Just A Little Boy
When I was just a little boy
Daddy brought me a brand new toy
Was a Derby fan on a piece of string
All I could do was kick his head in
You Reds
Kick his head in
You Reds
(A charming number for the fans at Derby County)

OLDHAM ATHLETIC

Come On, Oldham
Meat pie, sausage roll
Come on Oldham score a goal

When I Was Just A Little Boy
When I was just a little boy
I asked my mother what shall I be
Should I be Man U or OAFC
And here's what she said to me
"Wash your mouth out, son
Go fetch your father's gun
And shoot some Man U scum
Shoot some Man U scum"

My Old Man Said Be A Bolton Fan
My old man said be a Bolton fan
I said f*** off b*******, you're a c***
I'd rather f*** a bucket wth a large hole in it
than be a Bolton fan for half a minute
I f***ed it, I f***ed it
I f***ed and I f***ed
I f***ed it till I couldn't f*** no more
and I got more out of f****ed that bucket
than seeing Bolton score
(For bitter rivals Bolton Wanderers)

PLYMOUTH ARGYLE

West Country
West Country, la la la
West Country, la la la

We Are the Argyle
Travelling Round Country
drinking All Your Cider
der Der Der Der Der We Are the Argyle
der Der Der Der Der We Are the Argyle

PORT VALE

The Wonder of You
(Another old chart-topper is resurrected)

Port Vale Chant
Boing, boing, bag o' s***
(No love lost with West Brom)

Ever Since I Was A Young Boy
(To the tune of 'Pinball Wizard')
Ever since I was a young boy,
I went to watch the Vale,
from Shrewbury down to Bournemouth,
I must of seen 'em all,
but our great black and white team,
sure plays some mean football!

S**tin' on the City
(To the tune of 'Winter Wonderland')
Staffordshire
Are ya listening
To the song, we are singing
Walking along
Singing our songs
S**ttin' on the City as we go

Christmastime

(Sung to the tune 'Mistletoe and Wine')
Christmastime, valium and wine,
children indulging in serious crime,
with mum on the heroin, and dad snorting coke,
Christmas is magic when you support Stoke
(Sung for bitter rivals Stoke City)

In the Town Where I Was Born

(To the tune of 'Yellow Submarine')
In the town where I was born
there's a team we go to see
(go to see)
and we all had ten pints of ale
before we go and see the Vale!
(see the Vale)

We all p*** in a red and white hat red and white hat
We all p*** in a red and white hat red and white hat

PRESTON NORTH END

Preston Chant
How wide do you want the goals?

Old Blackpool Boys
Who's that jumping in the pier
Who's that drowning in the sea
It's the old Blackpool boys
Making all the f****** noise
'cos they can't beat the famous PNE

QUEENS PARK RANGERS

QPR Chant
And it's Queens Park Rangers
Queens Park Rangers FC
We're the finest football team
The world has ever seen

2–1
2–1, you only beat us 2–1
When everyone else scores three,
You only beat us 2--1
*(Man City's anthem 'Blue Moon' is thrown back at them after
they could only see off Rangers 2-1. The Londoners had
suffered eight straight defeats before this one)*

He's Only A Poor Little Spurs Fan
He's only a poor little Spurs fan
He stands at the back of the Shelf
He goes to the bar
To buy a laaaaaa-ger
But only buys one for himself

Tony Adams

Who's that driving on the pavement
Who's that crashing through the wall
He plays in red and white
And he crashes every night
Tony Adams is a donkey after all

Steve Morrow

Morr-ow, Morrow fell off
Morr-ow, Morrow fell off
Morr-ow, Morrow fell off
Morrow fell off a donkey
(One for Steve Morrow who jumped off
Tony Adams' back
in a game and broke his arm)

We Are the Rangers Boys

We are the Rangers boys
Stand up and make some noise
We know our manners
We fight with spanners
We are respected wherever we go
Doors and windows open wide (open wide)
You ever seen Charlton's big bald head
You ever seen Chelsea's poxy shed
We are the Rangers boys!

READING

Reading Chant
We support our local team
*(A dig at Man Utd's fans – most of whom
don't come from Manchester)*

You're Posh, But You're Not Royal
You're Posh, but you're not Royal
(Reading fans have a pop at Peterborough)

ROCHDALE

Dale
Daaaaa-le
Daaaaa-le
Daaaaa-le

Robbie Painter
Super, super Rob
Super, super Rob
Super, super Rob
Super Robbie Painter

All Hail!
Well, hail Lisa Stansfield,
Hail GracieFields, Julie Goodyear too.
All hail, hail cos we are the mighty Dale!
Famous over land and sea, feared from all around,
We hate Manchester and
Yorkshire too!

Can You Hear Bury Sing No No?
Can you hear Bury sing no no?
Can you hear Bury sing no no?
Can you here Bury sing?
I can't hear a f***ing thing
(*No doubting the local rivalry*)

We only cost 5 grand
We only cost 5 grand,
We only cost 5 grand,
We only cost 5 grand,
We only cost 5 grand
(Fans' joy at losing only 1–0 to
multi-millionaires Chelsea)

SCARBOROUGH

We're Going Up
We're going up, we're going up, we're going
Scarborough's going up

We Hate City
We hate City, and we hate City
We hate City, and we hate City
We hate City, and we hate City
We are the City Haters
(Neighbours and rivals feel the force of this one)

Tom Mooney
Trifle, trifle, trifle
Let's have a Mooney rifle
(Encouragement for former favourite Tom Mooney)

SCUNTHORPE UNITED

Any Old Iron
Any old Iron, any old Iron, we sing, 'Up the Iron'
You look sweet, walking down the street
Bottle in ya hand and boots on yer feet
Dressed in style, nice big smile, we sing, 'Up the Iron'
And we don't give a damn for a Grimsby fan
Old Iron, old Iron

Scunthorpe
With an S and a C and a U N T
H and an O and an R P E
U-N-I-T-E-D
Scunthorpe United ... FC

We're Scunthorpe
Forever and ever
We follow our team
We're Scunthorpe United
We rule supreme
We'll never be mastered
By you Yorkshire b**tards
We'll keep the Blue Flag flying high

SHEFFIELD UNITED

United Chant
I was walking down Shoreham Street singing a song
Along came a pig fan and asked what's wrong
I kicked him in the balls and I kicked him in the head
Now that Wednesday fan is dead

The Grease Chip Buttie
You fill up my senses
Like a gallon of Magnet
Like a packet of Woodbines
Like a good pinch of snuff
Like a night out in Sheffield
Like a greasy chip buttie
Oh Sheffield United
Come thrill me again

SHEFFIELD WEDNESDAY

Wednesday Chant
(To the theme tune of 'The Great Escape',
accompanied by the splendid Hillsborough band)

Di Canio
D-I-CAN-I-O
D-I-CAN-I-O

Singing the Blues
Never felt more like singing the Blues
Wednesday win, United lose
Oh Wednesday, you've got me singing the Blues

You Got Me Wandering Wednesday
Wednesday,
You got me wandering Wednesday,
You got me wandering Wednesday,
You got me wandering.

We Are the Owls
We are the Owls
And we follow our team all the way
There's only one team in Yorkshire
We're the famous Sheffield...Wednesday!

The Utrecht Song

Daaa, da da da daaaa, dadadada, dadadada
dadadadaaaa
Da da daaaa, da da daa daaaa
Da da daa, da da da daaaa
WEDNESDAY!
(First appeared at the friendly against
FC Utrecht, Holland, summer 1996)

At the Lane

At the Lane,
At the Lane,
Oh they're all f***ing w***ers at the Lane!
At the Lane.....
At the Lane.....
Oh they're all f***ing w***ers at the Lane...
(A jibe at city rival United whose ground is Bramall Lane)

David Pleat

That's neat that's neat that's neat that's neat
We really love that David Pleat

The Blue Flag

Forever and ever, we'll follow our team
Sheffield Wednesday, we are supreme
We'll never be mastered by no southern b**tards
We'll keep the Blue Flag flying high

Sheffield Wednesday Chant (1)

Sheeeee-field Wednesday
Hallelujah! Hallelujah!

Sheffield Wednesday Chant (2)

There'll be a commotion when we win promotion
So score, Weeeddddd-nesday score

Sheffield Is Wonderful

Oh Sheffield is wonderful
Oh Sheffield is wonderful
It's got tits, f***y and the Wednesday
Oh Sheffield is wonderful

You're All Just United Supporters!
You're all just United Supporters!
you're slaves to the red white and black!
we know it's a shame
that you've no one to blame
since you gave David Weir the sack!
yes you're all United supporters!
all mugs for lost causes art thou!
you hope it won't stay the same
one day they'll win a game,
yes one day your piggies will fly!
(Sung for the pleasure of bitter rivals Sheffield United)

It's Time To Put Your Boots On

It's time to put your boots on
It's time to drink your beer
It's time to put your fists up
'cos the Wednesday boys are here

We're Blue We're White

We're blue we're white
We're f***ing Wednesdayites,
You're red and white
And f***ing s*** and s**te

SHREWSBURY TOWN

We All Follow the Shrewsbury
We all follow the Shrewsbury
Over land and sea and Wrexham
We all follow the Shrewsbury
On to victory

My Old Man
My old man said follow the Town
And don't dilly dally on the way
We'll take the Station End and all that's in it
All get your boots on, we'll be there in a minute
With bottles and hammers, hatchets and spanners
We don't care what the f***ing coppers say
'Cos we are the boys from the Gay, Gay Meadow

SOUTHAMPTON

When the Saints Go Marching In

Oh when the Saints
Go marching in
Oh when the Saints go marching in
I want to be in that number
Oh when the Saints go marching in
Oh when the Saints
(Oh when the Saints)
Go marching in
(Go marching in)

If You All Hate Pompey Clap Your Hands

If you all hate Pompey, clap your hands
If you all hate Pompey, clap your hands
If you want everyone to know it,
Then let us all show it,
Clap your hands
(Some south coast rivalry with Portsmouth)

I Comes Down From Southampton

I can't read and I can't write
But that don't really matter
'Cos I comes down from Southampton
And I can drive a tractor

I can plough and milk a cow
And drive a great big mower
But the thing that I like best
Is being a strawberry grower
Oooooo-aaarrrrrrr
Oooooo-aaarrrrrrr
Ooooooo to be a Southernerrrrrrrrr

Matt Le Tissier

Le Tiss, Le Tiss
Matt Matt Le Tiss
He gets the ball, he takes the p***
Matt Matt Le Tiss

Oh Danny Boy

Oh Danny Boy,
The stripes, the stripes are calling
Over hill and down the mountainside,
We'll be here in sunshine or in shadow,
Oh Danny Boy, we love you so

SOUTHEND UNITED

Southend Pier

Oh Southend Pier
Is longer than yours
Oh Southend Pier is longer than yours
It's got some shops and a railway
Oh Southend Pier is longer than yours
*(Shrimpers supporters taunt fans of other teams
based in seaside resorts with this peculiar little number)*

I Woke Up This Morning Feeling Fine

(To the tune of 'I'm Into Something Good')
I woke up this morning feeling fine
Southend United on my mind
We play football the way, the way we should
Something tells me I'm into something good.

Sea! Sea! Seasiders!

Sea! Sea! Seasiders!
Sea! Sea! Seasiders!
Sea! Sea! Seasiders!
Sea! Sea! Seasiders!

Loyal Supporters

Loyal supporters de-de de-de de,
loyal supporters de-de de-de de,
loyal supporters de-de de-de de

We're In Debt

We're in debt, we're in debt and it's growing,
we're in debt, we're in debt, we can't pay.
we're in debt, we're in debt and it's growing,
we'll be bankrupt by the end of May,
and it's your fault,
and it's your fault,
and it's your fault you greedy b*stard,
and it's your fault,
and it's your fault,
and it's your fault you b*stard!

When Southend United Come Out to Play

When Southend United come out to play
Sing up, sing up,
When Southend United come out to play
Sing up, sing up,
When Southend United come out to play,
We follow them home and away,
We all follow the Essex boys in blue
Na na na na na na na na na na na na na na na na na
na na na na na na na na,
We all follow the Essex boys in blue

STEVENAGE FC

You Are S**t
(To the tune of 'I Can't Help Falling in Love With You')
You are s**t
And you always were
And we can't help scoring more goals that you

STOKE CITY

He's Big
He's big,
He's red
His feet stick out the bed
(Accolades for 6ft 7inches striker Peter Crouch)

Build A Bonfire
Build a bonfire
Build a bonfire
Put Crewe on the top
Put the Vale in the middle
and burn the f***ing lot
*(A hot welcome for Crewe Alexandra and Port Vale
supporters, both local rival Potteries' clubs)*

We're the Best Behaved Supporters in the League

We're the best behaved supporters in the league,
We're the best behaved supporters in the league
We're the best behaved supporters in the league
We're the best behaved supporters in the league
Best behaved supporters,
Best behaved supporters in the league
We're a right bunch of b*st*rds when we lose,
We're a right bunch of b*st*rds when we lose
We're a right bunch of b*st*rds,
Right bunch of b*st*rds,
A right bunch of b*st*rds when we lose

Asmir Begovic

(To the tune of Simon and Garfunkel's 'Mrs Robinson')
Here's to you Asmir Begovic, City loves you more than you will
know, woaaaahhhh
Here's to you Asmir Begovic, City loves you more than you will
know, woaaaahhh.
(Stoke City fans to their beloved former goalkeeper)

SUNDERLAND

Cheer Up Peter Reid

(To the tune of 'Daydream Believer')

Oh I could fly without wings
On the back of Reidy's kings
At three o'clock I'm happy as can be
'Cos the good times they are here
And the Premiership is near
So watch out world as all of Roker sings

Cheer up Peter Reid
Oh what can it mean
To a Sunderland supporter
To be top of the League

We once thought of you
As a Scouser dressed in blue
Now you're red and white through and through
We had all dreamt of the day
When a saviour would come our way
And now we know our dreams are coming true

I'm A Believer (of Lee Clark) Classic Chant
(To the tune of 'I'm A Believer')
I thought class was only true
in the Premier League, Lee Clark
Meant for other fans, but not for us
Lee was ready for England
That's the way it seemed
One-touch football beating other teams

Then I saw him play,
now I'm a believer
Not a trace of mag in his genes
I'm in love, Oooooooooh!
I'm a believer
I couldn't boo him if I tried

I thought goals were more or less never seen
in the Premier League, Lee Clark
But the more he played the more we got
Oh yes!

What's the use in trying
All you get is pain
When you try to stop Clarkie playing his game

Then I saw him play,
now I'm a believer
Not a trace of mag in his genes
I'm in love, Oooooooooh!
I'm a believer
I couldn't boo him if I tried

F*** 'Em All

F*** 'em all, f*** 'em all
Dalglish McDermott and Hall
We'll never be mastered by black and white b**tards
'Cos Sunderland's the best of them all

Top of the League

(To the tune of 'Top of the World')
We're on the
Top of the League looking
Down on the others
And the only explanation I can see
Is that one Peter Reid
Is all that we need
'Cos he took us to the top of the League

All We Are Saying

(To the tune of John Lennon's 'Give Peace a Chance')
All we are saying
Is give us 3 points...

All We Want is a Decent Referee

All we want is a decent referee
(clap clap)
A decent referee
(clap clap)
A decent referee
(clap clap)
All we want is a decent referee

You Sexy Thing

(To the tune of 'I Believe in Miracles')
I believe in miracles, Niall Quinn
You sexy thing

I believe in long balls
Since you came along, Niall Quinn

You're always injured Quinny
How did you know we'd put up with you?

How did you know we needed goals so badly?
How did you know, we'd sing for you gladly?

Yesterday, you were just a six-foot Irishman
Now you're putting headers away, scoring every match.

I believe in miracles, Niall Quinn
You sexy thing

I believe in long balls
Since you came along, Niall Quinn

You're always injured Quinny
But when you're not, you're our best hope

Yesterday, you were just a six-foot Irishman
Now you're putting headers away, scoring every match

I believe in miracles, Niall Quinn
You sexy thing

I believe in long balls
Since you came along, Niall Quinn

I Wish They All Could Be
(To the tune of 'California Girls')
Southwick girls are sexy
And the Hylton girls are hip
And the Farringdon girls are foxy
When they're giving you their lip

Downhill girls are daring
And the Tunstall girls are tops
And you can't go wrong
With Suzy Wong
And she comes from Marley Potts

I wish they all could be from Sunderland
I wish they all could be from Sunderland
I wish they all could be Sunderland girls

SWANSEA

Always S*** on the English Side of the Bridge
Always s*** on the English side of the bridge
da da da da da da da da
(Welsh vitriol for the English)

You Better Stick to Your Racing
You better stick to your racing,
stick to your racing,
stick to your racing,
you better stick to you racing
(Special for victories over Cheltenham)

TORQUAY UNITED

Jack, Jack, Jack
(To the tune of 'Hot, Hot Hot')
O-way, O-way
O-way, O-way
Rodney Jack Jack Jack

One Team in Devon
One team in Devon, there's only one team in Devon

I'm Torquay Until I Die
*(To the tune of 'H.A.P.P.Y', theme of the
1970s sitcom* Only When I Laugh)
I'm Torquay 'til I die
I'm Torquay 'til I die
I know I am I'm sure I am
I'm Torquay 'til I die

Everywhere we go!

(Lead) Everywhere we go!

(Crowd) Everywhere we go!

(Lead) People wanna know!

(Crowd) People wanna know!

(Lead) Who we are!

(Crowd) Who we are!

(Lead) Where we come from!

(Crowd) Where we come from!

(Lead) This is what we tell them!

(Crowd) This is what we tell them!

(Lead) We all come from Torquay!

(Crowd) We all come from Torquay!

(Lead) And were the yellow army!

(Crowd) And were the yellow army!

(Lead) YELLOW ARMY!

(Crowd) YELLOW ARMY!

(All) YELLOW ARMY!

TOTTENHAM HOTSPUR

We Are the Tottenham
We are the Tottenham, the pride of the South
We hate the Arsenal, 'cos they are all mouth
We took the North Bank, and that was f*** all
The Tottenham will rise and the Arsenal will fall

Classic Jürgen Klinsmann Chant
He flies through the air with the greatest of ease
He never got touched, but he's down on his knees
(In honour of Jürgen Klinsmann)

Classic Nayim Chant
Nayim, from the halfway line
Nayim, from the halfway line
*(Ex-Spur who gunned down Arsenal with a spectacular goal
for Real Zaragoza in the dying seconds of the 1995 European
Cup-Winners' Cup Final)*

Classic George Graham Chant
Georgie Graham's magic
He wears a magic hat
And when he saw the agent's bung
He said I'm having that

He's Only A Poor Little Gooner

He's only a poor little Gooner
He stands at the back of the Bank
He watches the reds, the football he dreads
So he ends up having a w***

He's only a poor little Gooner
His face is all tattered and torn
He made me feel sick, so I hit him with a brick
And now he don't sing anymore

Stand Up If You Hate Stewards

Stand up if you hate stewards
Stand up if you hate stewards

You're Not Fit to Wear the Shirt

You'rrrreeee not fit to wear the shirt
You're not fit to wear the shirt

We Hate Arsenal
We hate Arsenal and we hate Arsenal
We hate Arsenal and we hate Arsenal
We hate Arsenal and we hate Arsenal
We are the Arsenal Haters

Classic "Hoddle, Hoddle, Hoddle, Hoddle" Chant
Hoddle, Hoddle, Hoddle, Hoddle,
Born is the King of White Hart Lane
(An old favourite for when Hoddle was a player and manager)

Supercalifragilistic
Supercalifragilistic Roman Pavlyuchenko
Tottenham Hotspur's number 9
is better than Shevchenko
Like Russians, always has a vodka
in his Kenco
Supercalifragilistic Roman Pavlyuchenko

TRANMERE ROVERS

Oh Birkenhead

Oh Birkenhead
Is wonderful
Oh Birkenhead is won-der-ful
Full of tits and fannies and the Rovers
Oh Birkenhead is wonderful

We Hate Scousers

We hate Scousers

We Are Not Scousers

Do not be mistaken, do not be misled
We are not Scousers, we're from Birkenhead
You can keep your cath-e-der-al
And Pier Head
We are not Scousers
We're from Birkenhead

WATFORD

All the Lads and All the Lovely Ladies
(To the tune of 'Blaydon Races')
All the lads and all the lovely ladies,
Going down to Vicarage
Rooooaaaaaddddddd..............
To see the Watford aces

Agadoo-do-do
Agadoo-do-do,
We're the Watford wrecking crew,
To the left, to the right,
Luton Town are f***ing sh*te!

Watford Chant
Elton John's Taylor-made army

We All Follow the Watford
Hello, Hello
We the golden boys
Hello, Hello
We are the golden boys,
So if you are a Luton fan
Surrender or you'll die

WEST BROMWICH ALBION

WBA Chant
Boing boing Baggies, boing boing

The Lord's My Shepherd
The Lord's my shepherd
I'll not want
He makes me down to lie
In pastures green
He leadeth me
The quiet waters by

Stand Up, If You've Bought the League
Stand up, if you've bought the League
Stand up, if you've bought the League
Stand up, if you've bought the League
Stand up, if you've bought the League!
*(A poke at the Abramovich fortune that
brought success to Chelsea)*

WEST HAM UNITED

'Allo 'Allo
'Allo 'allo
We are the Cockney boys
'Allo 'allo
We are the Cockney boys
And if you're a Millwall fan,
Surrender or you die
We all follow United!

I'm Forever Blowing Bubbles
I'm forever blowing bubbles,
Pretty bubbles in the air,
They fly so high,
Nearly reach the sky,
Then like my dreams,
They fade and die.
Fortune's always hiding,
I've looked everywhere,
I'm forever blowing bubbles,
Pretty bubbles in the air
(This has been West Ham's theme since the 1930s

Ian Wright
Ian W***, w***, w***

(Pre 1998-99 season. Former Arsenal striker Ian Wright always had a habit of scoring against the Hammers)

Classic Alvin Martin Chant
Alvin Martin,
Alvin Martin,
Alvin Alvin Martin,
He's got no hair,
But we don't care
Alvin Alvin Martin

WIGAN ATHLETIC

You Can Stick Yer F***ing Rugby Up Yer A***
You can stick yer f***ing rugby up yer a***
You can stick yer f***ing rugby up yer a***
You can stick yer f***ing rugby
You can stick yer f***ing rugby
Stick yer f***ing rugby up yer a***
(Friendly fire for the fans of Wigan Rugby League Club)

Merry Christmas
So here it is
Merry Christmas
Everybody's having fun
Bollocks to you Preston c***s
We've beaten you 2–1
*(Slade's Christmas party anthem is used to spread
a little seasonal cheer among Wigan's rivals)*

Build A Bonfire
(To the tune of 'My Darling Clementine')
Build a bonfire, build a bonfire
Stick Preston on the top
Put Burnley in the middle
And burn the f***ing lot

You Are My Sunshine
You are my sunshine, my only sunshine
You make me happy, when skies are blue
I never notice, how much I miss you
Until they take my sunshine away

WYCOMBE WANDERERS

A Decent Referee
(To the tune of 'Yellow Submarine')
All we want is a decent referee
A decent referee, a decent referee

La, La, La, La, La La La, La La, La, La
La, la, la, la, la la la, la la la, la, la,
La, la la, la, la, la la la la,
We all f***ing hate Slough

Chairboys' Barmy Army
Chairboys' barmy army,
Chairboys' barmy army,
Chairboys' barmy army

YORK CITY

York Chant (1)
Are you Scarborough in disguise?

We Don't Wanna Follow Scarboro
We don't wanna follow Scarboro,
We don't wanna follow Leeds,
We'd rather hang around
Near Kings Cross underground,
Watching all the strippers in the
Flying Scotsman,
We don't wanna follow Man Utd,
We'd rather have our b****ks shot away
'Cos we all follow City
Super super City and we'll be there
Wherever City play

Y-R-A
Y-R-A, we're Yorkshire's Republican Army
We're barmy wherever we go
We fight friend and foe
'Cos we are the Y-R-A

York Chant (2)
What's it like to be outclassed?
*(Three classics born out of the Coca-Cola Cup
triumph over Alex Ferguson's troops)*

York Chant (3)
Red army, red army, red army

You're Going in the Ouse
You're going in the Ouse, you're going in the Ouse
And now you're gonna believe us
And now you're gonna believe us
You're going in the Ouse
*(The Minstermen's faithful offer visitors an unexpected
chance to sample the delights of the city's river)*

The Pride of all Yorkshire
We are the pride of all Yorkshire, the cock of the North
We hate Leeds United and Scarborough, of course
We kick in the 'Boro until they go down
'Cos the City boys are in town

Third Division Rubbish
Third Division rubbish, you're Third Division rubbish

We're North Yorkshire's Only One
North Yorkshire's only one
North Yorkshire's only one
And are you going to believe us
We're North Yorkshire's only one

SCOTTISH CLUB SONGS

CELTIC

The Celtic Song

Hail, Hail, the Celts are here
What the hell do we care
What the hell do we care
Hail, Hail, the Celts are here
What the hell do we care now ...

For it's a grand old team to play for
For it's a grand old team to see
And if you know the history
It's enough to make your heart go
Nine-in-a-row

We don't care what the animals say
What the hell do we care
For all we know
Is that there's going to be a show
And that Glasgow Celtic will be there

Celtic is the Name

In Glasgow town we have a team and Celtic is the name
We've beaten Rangers and Milan for Celtic know the game
And if you don't believe me, boys,
then come and see us play
For Glasgow Celtic, up the Celtic, beats the world today
For Glasgow Celtic, up the Celtic, beats the world today

We are a famous football team I'm sure you all agree
We've played them all, the big and small,
from Lisbon to Dundee
And if you don't believe me, boys, then this to you I say
Come up the Parkhead, dear old Parkhead,
Celtic leads the way
Come up the Parkhead, dear old Parkhead,
Celtic leads the way

In Glasgow town we have a team and Celtic is the name
We've beaten Rangers and Milan for Celtic know the game
And if you don't believe me, boys,
then come and see us play
For Glasgow Celtic, up the Celtic, beats the world today
For Glasgow Celtic, up the Celtic, beats the world today

The Coronation Cup

Said Lizzie to Philip as they sat down to dine
I've just had a note from a good friend of mine
His name is big Geordie, he's loyal and true
And his big dirty nose is a bright shade of blue

He says that the Rangers are right on their game
And he asks for a trophy to add to their fame
We'll send them a trophy that the Rangers can win
Said Philip to Lizzie, Watch the Celts don't step in

Said Lizzie to Philip they don't stand a chance
I'll send up my Gunners to lead them a dance
With the Celtic defeated, the way will be clear
And a trophy for the Rangers in my crowning year

Alas, and alas, for the wearers of blue
The Celts beat the Arsenal and the Manchester too
Beat Hibs in the final, and lo and behold
All of Hampden was covered in green, white and gold

Said Lizzie to Philip when she heard the news
So tell me dear Philip, for you ought to know
How to beat Glasgow Celtic and keep them below

Said Philip to Lizzie, there's only one way
And I've known the secret for many a day
To beat Glasgow Celtic, you'll have to deport
All the fighting mad Irish that give them support

The Flags Are Out For Celtic

The flags are gaily flying o'er Celtic Park today
Because the lads of Celtic have shown the world the way
They played the game in Lisbon and here is how they won
They didn't play defensive, attack is what they done

The flags are out for Celtic, they know just what to do
And Scottish hearts and Irish hearts are
mighty proud of you

In all the big world over the name of Celtic rung
And in our heart of Glasgow our Celtic song was sung
God bless you great XI, this is our greatest day
Next season Jock from Greenock we're with
you all the way

The flags are out for Celtic, they know just what to do
And Scottish hearts and Irish hearts are
mighty proud of you

You won so many cups this year, four or five or six
You should give one to Rangers, they're really in a fix
John Lawrence shook your hands, lads, as
you came off the plane
And everyone is proud of you, your football brought
you fame

The flags are out for Celtic, they know just what to do
And Scottish hearts and Irish hearts are
mighty proud of you

DUNDEE

Top of the League
You know, you know
We're top of the League and you're no'
You know, you know
We're top of the League and you're no'
Top of the League, oh yes, we're top of the League
We're top of the League and you're no'

As I Was Walking
As I was walking down the Overgate
I met wee Tommy Scobie
And he said to me,
"Would you like to see the famous Dundee FC?'

So we went along to Dens Park
To see the famous XI
But when we got there
The terracing was bare
And we'd gave United seven

DUNDEE UNITED

The Dens Park Massacre of '65
Get down on your knees and pray
It's the anniversary
Of the Dens Park massacre of '65 (65!)
It's the day we won't forget
And the Dundee will regret
It's the day we gave them 1-2-3-4-5!

It was the 11th of September
A day we all remember
Finn Dossing was at centre and scored three
Lennart Wing from the spot
And Gillespie with a shot
A shot that Ally Packy didn't see

United Boys
Hello! Hello! We are United boys
Hello! Hello! You'll tell us by our noise
We're up to our knees in Derry boys
Surrender or you'll die
For we are United boys

Let's All Laugh At Dundee
Let's all laugh at Dundee
Haha ha ha, haha ha ha

HEARTS

I Was Born Under An Orange Scarf
(To the tune of 'I Was Born Under A Wandering Star')
I was born under an orange scarf
I was born under an orange scarf
Do you know where hell is?
Hell is Easter Road
Heaven is Tynecastle
Where the Fenians crap their load
Oh, I was born under an orange scarf

We're Going to Europe
(To the tune of 'My Way')
And now, the end is near
We've followed Hearts, from Perth to Paisley
We've travelled far, by bus and car
And other times, we've went by railway
We've been, to Aberdeen
We hate the Hibs, they make us spew up
So make a noise you Gorgie Boys
We're going to Europe

HMFC

To see HMFC
We'll even dig the Channel Tunnel
When we're afloat on some big boat
We'll tie our scarves around the funnel
We have no cares for other players
Like Rossi, Boniek or Tardelli
When we're overseas the Hibs will be
In Portobelly
The might of Europe

We all can laugh at Hibs
When we play Chelsea, Metz or Inter
They'll be up at Dundee
And relegated by mid-winter
While we go marching on
And show the Huns the way to do it
They lost again while we had slain
The might of Europe

The day's not far away
When we will reach the heights of glory
We'll follow Hearts through foreign parts
And Gorgie Boys will tell the story
How we scored three at Napoli
Hibs lost away again at Greenock
When Hibs went down we took the crown
As Kings of Europe

H-E-A-R-T-S

Away up in Gorgie at Tynecastle Park
There's a wee fitba' team that will aye make its mark
They've won all the honours in footballing arts
And there's no other team to compare with the Hearts

H-E-A-R-T-S
If you cannae spell it then here's what it says
Hearts, Hearts, glorious Hearts
It's down at Tynecastle they bide
The talk of the toon are the boys in maroon
And Auld Reekie supports them with pride

This is my story, this is my song
Follow the Hearts and you can't go wrong
Oh some say that Celtic and Rangers are grand
But the boys in maroon are the best in the land

We've won the League flag and we've won the League Cup
Though we sometimes go down we can aye go back up
Our forwards can score and it's no idle talk
Our defence is as strong as the auld castle rock

National caps we can always supply
Like Massey and Walker and Bauld and Mackay
If I had the time I could name dozens more
Who've helped in producing the auld Hampden roar

The Fields of Athenry

By a lonely prison wall, I heard a young girl calling
Michael they have taken you away
For you stole Travelyan's corn,
so the young might see the morn
Now a prison ship lies waiting in the bay

Low lie the Fields of Athenry
Where once we watched the small, free birds fly
Our love was on the wing,
we had dreams and songs to sing
It's so lonely on the Fields of Athenry

By a lonely prison wall, I heard the young man calling
Nothing matters Mary when you are free
Against the famine and the crown,
I rebelled they cut me down
Now you must raise our child in dignity

By a lonely harbour wall, she watched the last star falling
As the prison ship sailed out against the sky
Now she'll wait and hope and pray,
for her love in Botany Bay
It's so lonely round the Fields of Athenry

PARTICK THISTLE

Mary from Maryhill
I love a lassie
A bonny bonny lassie
She's as thin as the paper on the wall
Legs like a spider
I'd like to f***in' ride her
Mary from Maryhill

RANGERS

The Sash

For it's here I am an Orangeman, just come across the sea
For singing and for dancing, I hope that I'll please thee
I can sing and dance with any man, as I did in days of yore
And its on the twelfth I long to wear
the sash my father wore

It is old but it is beautiful and its colours they are fine
It was worn at Derry, Aughrim, Enniskillen and the Boyne
My Father wore it as a youth in bygone days of yore
And its on the twelfth I long to wear,
the sash my father wore

For it's now I'm going to leave you, good luck to you I'll say
And when I'm on the ocean deep, I hope for me you'll pray
I'm going to my native land, to a place they call Dromore,
Where on the twelfth I long to wear
the sash my father wore

Whenever I come back again my brethren here to see
I hope to find old Orange style, they will always welcome me
My favourite tune's 'Boyne Water',
but to please me more and more,
And make my Orange heart full glad with
the sash my father wore

The Sash (2)

It is old but it is beautiful, it's red, it's white and it's blue
It's worn on the slopes of Ibrox Park, and a place called
Parkhead too
My father wore it as a youth in the bygone days of yore
And it's on display every Saturday
Every time the Rangers score

The Famous Royal Blue

For ever and ever, we'll follow the Gers
The Glasgow Rangers, the Teddy Bears
For we will be mastered, by whom, by no Fenian b**tards
We'll keep the Blue Flag flying high

Soooooo, bring on the Hibs, the Hearts, the Celtic
Bring on the Spaniards by the score
Barcelona, Real Madrid
Who the hell are you trying to kid
For we're out to show the world what we can do

I have often heard that Real Madrid is the greatest football team
I have even heard that Anderlecht, is the best you have ever seen
There's Manchester United, and there's Tottenham Hotspur, too
There is Everton, Burnley, Blackbum, just to name a famous few

Who's that team we call the Rangers
Who's that team we all adore
They're the boys in royal blue and they are
Scotland's gallant few
And we are out to show the world what we can do

Soooooo bring on the Hibs, the Hearts, the Celtic
Bring on Spaniards by the score
And we will hope that every game, we will imortalize
the name
Of the boys that wear the Famous Royal Blue

The Billy Boys
Hello, hello, we are the Billy Boys
Hello, hello, you'll know us by our noise
We're up to our necks in Fenian blood
Surrender or you'll die
'Cos we are the Bridgestown Boys

CLASSIC SONGS

The Wheels On Your House
The wheels on your house go round and round,
round and round
(Directed at fans who are perceived as caravans)

He's Got A Dry Scalp
He's got a dry scalp, He's got a dry scalp,
That boy Joe Hart, He's got a dry scalp!
*(QPR fans ridicule Joe Hart for
appearing in a shampoo advert)*

Giggs Will Tear You Apart
Giggs, Giggs will tear you apart…
*(Manchester United's fans paean to Ryan Giggs, to the tune of
'Love will tear us apart')*

Park, Park Wherever You May Be
Park, park wherever you may be,
You eat dogs in your country,
It could be worse, you could be scouse,
Eating rats in your council house
(Man Utd fans chanting against Liverpool fans)

Sunday, Monday, Habib Beye

Sunday, Monday, Habib Beye. Tuesday, Wednesday,
Habib Beye. Thursday, Friday, Habib Beye. Saturday,
Habib Beye, rockin' all week with you!
*(Sung by Newcastle United fans at St James' Park
to the tune of 'Happy Days' theme)*

He's Red, He's Sound, He's Banned From Every Ground

He's red, he's sound, he's banned from every ground,
Carra's dad, Carra's dad.
*(Sung by Liverpool fans about Jamie Carragher's father, who
was arrested at a match for being drunk)*

There's Only One Carlton Palmer

There's only one Carlton Palmer, and he smokes marijuana.
He's six foot tall and his head's too small,
Livin' in a Palmer wonderland!
*(Stockport County fans singing about their
manager Carlton Palmer in 2002)*

He Cheats, He Dives

He cheats, He dives,
He hates the Jackson Five,
Luis Suárez, Luis Suárez
*(Sung by opposing teams following accusations of racism
and unprofessional conduct against Luis Suarez)*

The Bill
It's just like watching The Bill!
(Blackburn fans singing about the large
amount of police at Ewood Park)

You're Shish
You're shish, and you know you are!
(Sung by Chelsea fans when their side played
Turkish Club, Galatasaray)

Who Let the Frogs Out?
Who let the frogs out?
Who? who? who? who?
(Leicester City fans sang this to the tune of 'Who Let the Dogs
Out' by the Baha Men when playing Arsenal who
notoriously had many French players)

Stuck in the Middle Giroud
Podolski to the left of me,
Walcott to the right, here I am,
Stuck in the middle Giroud!
(Arsenal fans chanting about their team to the tune of the
'Stuck in the Middle With You')

He Sleeps in Fergie's Bed
He's bald, he's red,
He sleeps in Fergie's bed!
Howard Webb, Howard Webb!
(Liverpool fans against Howard Webb and Alex Ferguson)

Stand Up If You Pay Your Tax

Stand up if you pay your tax

(A chant aimed at Harry Redknapp by various football teams after he was investigated for tax fraud)

Mourinho! Mourinho! Mourinho!

Oh the weather outside is frightful,
But the goals are so delightful,
Stamford Bridge is the place to go,
Mourinho! Mourinho! Mourinho!

(Chelsea fans sing this to the tune of 'Let It Snow')

Santi C Is Coming To Town

You'd better watch out, you'd better not cry, you'd better be good
I'm telling you why...'cos Santi C is coming to town.

(Arsenal supporters sang to Santi Cazorla, to the tune of 'Santa Claus Is Coming To Town')

The City's All Yours

The city's all yours, The city's all yours,
While we're in Europe, The city's all yours!

(Birmingham fans mock Aston Villa whilst they were in Europe)

U-N-I-T-E-D

U-N-I-T-E-D
That spells f****** debt to me
With a knick knack paddawack give a dog a bone
Ocean Finance on the phone
(Manchester City fans taunting Manchester United fans)

Away in a Manger
Away in a manger,
No crib for a bed,
The little lord Jesus woke up and he said,
We hate Wrexham
*(Chester City's Christmas chant to the
tune of 'Away In A Manger')*

Twelve Days of Christmas
On the 12th day of Christmas my true love gave to me,
12 David Hodgson, 11 Graeme Souness, 10 Craig Johnston,
9 Ian Rush, 8 Sammy Lee, 7 Kenny Dalglish, 6 Alan Hansen,
5 Ronnie Whelan, 4 Mark Lawrenson, 3 Barney Rubble,
2 Philip Neal, And Brucie in our goal!
*(Liverpool's greatest line-up, sung to the
tune of 'The 12 Days Of Christmas')*

He's Big, He's Fast
(To the tune of 'Quartermaster's Store')

He's big, he's fast, his first name should come last,
Stern John, Stern John
*(Former Birmingham striker Stern John was
the target of this chant)*

Two Andy Gorams
Two Andy Gorams....
There's only two Andy Gorams
*(Rangers goalkeeper Andy Goram was revealed to be mildly
schizophrenic; fans chanted this to the tune of 'Guantanamera')*

Ooh-aah Cantona
Ooh aah Cantona, say ooh ahh Cantona!
*(Started by Leeds fans, nicked by Man Utd fans when Eric
Cantona played there. Then fans started singing 'Ou est
Cantona?' to mournful Leeds fans)*

The Greatest
(To the tune of 'The Wild Rover')
And it's *[insert team name]*
[insert team name] FC
We're by far the greatest team
The world has ever seen

Can We Play You Every Week
Can we play you
Can we play you
Can we play you every week?

We'll Never Play You Again
We'll never play you again
(Sung by fans of teams who know they are moving up to the next league at the end of a season)

You're Supposed To Be At Home
You're supposed to,
You're supposed to,
You're supposed to be at home,
You're supposed to be at home
(A popular chant from away fans, when they're competing for who's loudest with their hosts)

Can You Hear?

Can you here the S***ty sing?
No-oh
No-oh
Can you here the S***ty sing?
No-oh
No-oh
Can you hear the S***ty sing?
'Cos I can't hear a f***ing thing
Oh-oh the S***ty
Ahhhhhhhhhhhhhhhhhh!
(Used for any team who include City in their name)

Referee Songs

(1)
The referee's a w***er

(2)
Who's the b**tard in the black?

(3)
Who's the b**tard in the green?
(Introduced when the referees' shirts changed)

We Shall Not Be Moved

We shall not
We shall not be moved
We shall not
We shall not be moved
We've got the team, the score
to win the Football League*
We shall not be moved
*(*Can be sung 'FA Cup' too)*

Let's Pretend We Scored A Goal

Let's pretend we scored a goal
Let's pretend we scored a goal

You'll Get the Sack in the Morning

Sack in the morning,
you'll get the sack in the morning
(Sung by fans, directed at the losing team's manager, to the tune of 'Guantanamera')

We Had Joy

We had joy, we had fun
We had *[insert team name]* on the run
But the joy couldn't last
'Cos the b**tards ran too fast

We're Gonna Score One More Than You

We're gonna score one more than you, doo-dah doo-dah
We're gonna score one more than you, doo-a-doo-dah-day

Brazil

Bra-zil
It's just like watching Brazil
It's just like watching Brazil
It's just like watching Brazil
Bra-zil
*(When a team is dominating and playing good football, this is
traditional for their fans to sing, to the tune of 'Blue Moon')*

Score in a Brothel
Score in a brothel
You couldn't score in a brothel

Who Ate All the Pies
Who ate all the pies?
Who ate all the pies?
You fat b**tard, you fat b**tard
You ate all the pies

You Only Live Round the Corner
You only live round the corner
*(To London and southern-based
Manchester United supporters)*

Glory, Glory
Glory, Glory *[team name]*
*(The "Glory, Glory" phrase originates from 'The Battle
Hymn of the Republic' from the American Civil War)*

If You All Hate Your Rivals, Clap Your Hands
If you all hate *[rival team]*, clap your hands
(To the tune of 'She'll Be Coming Round The Mountain')

You're Not Singing Anymore
(To the tune of 'Guide Me, O Thou Great Jehovah')
You're not sing-ing, you're not sing-ing,
you're not sing-ing any-more

Let Him Die
Let him die, let him die, let him die
(Sympathy for the injured opposing player)

You're Gonna Get ...
You're gonna get your f***in' heads kicked in

You're So S***
You're so s*** it's unbelievable

Let's All Have A Disco
Let's all have a disco
Lets's all have a disco
La, la, la, la, Oi
La, la, la, la, Oi

There's Only One...
One *[player's name]*, there's only one *[player's name]*

I Want To Go Home
(To the tune of 'Sloop John B')
I want to go home, I want to go hoo-oome,
[Town name]'s a s***hole, I want to go home

Que Sera Sera

(Que Sera Sera, from the 1956 Hitchock film The Man Who Knew Too Much, *sung by Doris Day)*

Que sera, sera
Whatever will be, will be
We're going to Wem-ber-ley
Que sera, sera

What's the Score?

Goalie, goalie, what's the score
Goalie, goalie, what's the score
*(Generally directed at the opposition goalkeeper
– if you're winning!)*

We Love You, We Do

We love you *[team-name]* we do
We love you *[team-name]* we do
We love you *[team-name]* we do
Oh *[team-name]* we love you
*(To the tune of 'We Love you Conrad' from the
1963 musical* Bye Bye Birdie*)*

Viva!

(To the tune of 'Pop Goes The World')
Viva *[player's name]*, viva *[player's name]*, playing on the wing,
hear *[team name]* sing, viva *[player's name]*

We Love You!

(To the theme of 'I Will Follow Him')
We love you! We love you! We love you!
And where you go we'll follow!...

Go West

(To the tune of 'Go West', originally by the Village People)
Goal-line and you f***ed it up

Who Are Ya?

Who are ya, Who are ya?
We're by far the greatest team

You've Only Got One Song!

One song!
You've only got one song!
You've only got one song!
You've only got one song!

NATIONAL TEAM SONGS

ENGLAND

Inger-land

Inger-land, Inger-land, Inger-land
Inger-land, Inger-land, Inger-land
Inger-land, Inger-land, Inger-land
Inger-land
INGER-LAND
(Repeat for most of the match)

Time To Blame the Referee

Time to blame the referee
*(Sung by English fans to losing teams, who put their team's
performance down to bad refereeing)*

If It Wasn't For...

If it wasn't for the English, you'd be Krauts
If it wasn't for the English, you'd be Krauts
If it wasn't for the English
Wasn't for the English
If it wasn't for the English, you'd be Krauts
(Often sung when England play France)

Rule Britannia

Rule Britannia
Britannia rules the waves
Britains never never never shall be slaves

The Great Escape

Da-da, da-da da
Da-da, da-da da
Da-da, da-da da-da da-darrr
ENGLAND!
(Repeat for most of the match)

Two World Wars

Two World Wars and one World Cup
Doo dar, doo dar
Two World Wars and one World Cup
Doo dar, doo dar day
(Still sung by fans when Germans are near)

God Save the Queen

Long live our noble Queen,
God save the Queen,
No surrender!
Send her victorious,
Happy and glorious,
Long to reign over us:
God save the Queen...

Keep St George In My Heart
Keep St George in my heart, keep me English,
Keep St. George in my heart I pray,
Keep St George in my heart, keep me English,
Keep me English till my dying day!

We Won the World Cup
We won the World Cup,
We won the World Cuuuuuup,
In sixty six,
We won the World Cup...

Jerusalem
And did those feet in ancient time,
Walk upon England's mountains green,
And was the holy lamb of God,
On England's pleasant pastures seen...

I'd Rather Be a Turnip Than A Swede
Oh I'd rather be a turnip than a swede,
Oh I'd rather be a turnip than a swede,
Oh I'd rather be a turnip,
Rather be a turnip,
Rather be a turnip than a swede...
(Sung to Swedish fans)

You're S***

You're s***,
But you're birds are fit,
You're s***,
But you're birds are fit,
(Sung to Ukraine fans)

I Am An English Man

(To the tune of 'I wanna be Anarchy')
I am an English man,
I am an England fan
I know what I want and the Lions will win it,
I wanna restore national pride,
'Coz Iiiiiiiiii,
Wanna beee,
Wayne Rooney...

We Want Our Beckham Back

(To the tune of 'Rapper's Delight')
We want our Beckham back,
I said we want our Beckham back,
We want our Beckham back,
I said we want our Beckham back...

Remember When We Had Sven

Remember when we had Sven,
At least we had Beckham then,
Now even Wayne can't score
Please don't put us through any more
(Sung by disheartened fans when England are losing)

SCOTLAND

Ally's Army
We're on the drugs with Ally's Army
We're all taking Benzadrine
And we'll really shake them up
When we drink it out of a cup
'Cos Scotland are the greatest football team

Deep Fry Yer Pizzas
Deep fry yer pizzas, we're gonna deep fry yer pizzas
*(Scotland fans made this threat against Italy's
cuisine in a World Cup qualifier)*

William Wallace

Scots, wha hae wi' Wallace bled
Scots, wham Bruce has aften led
Welcome to your gory bed
Or to victory

We Hate Coca-Cola

(To the tune of 'Guantanamera')
We hate Coca-Cola
We hate Fanta, too
We're the Tartan Army
And we love Irn Bru

Loch Lomond

By yon bonnie bank and by yon bonnie braes
Where the sun shines bright on Loch Lomond
Where me and my true love were ever wont to gae
On the bonnie, bonnie banks of Loch Lomond

For you'll take the high road and I'll take the low road
And I'll be in Scotland afore ye
Where me and my true love will never meet again
By the bonnie, bonnie banks of Loch Lomond

We Hate England

We hate England,
We hate England,
We hate England more than you!
We hate England more than you!"

There's Only One Team in Tallinn

One team in Tallinn
There's only one team in Tallinn
There's only one team in Tallinn
*(Sung by the Tartan Army when Estonia failed to turn up for
their 1996 World Cup qualifier in the Estonian capital)*

Hokey Cokey

You put your left hand in
You take your left hand out
You put your left hand in and you shake it all about
You do the hokey cokey and you turn around
That's what it's all about
Oh Diego Maradona
Oh Diego Maradona
Oh Diego Maradona
He put the English out, out, out

Stand up

Stand up if you hate England
Stand up if you hate England
Stand up if you hate England

Sing When You're Whaling

Sing when you're whaling
You only sing when you're whaling
*(Sung by the Tartan Army when Scotland played
Norway in the 1998 World Cup finals)*

Where's Yer Father?

Where's yer father
Where's yer father
Where's yer father, referee?

Yi havna got one
Yi havna got one
Yir a b**tard referee

Famous Tartan Army

We're the famous Tartan Army and we're off to gay Paree
Gay Paree
Gay Paree
We're the famous Tartan Army and we're off to gay Paree

Everywhere We Go

Everywhere we go
People want to know
Who we are
So we're gonna tell them
We're mental and we're barmy
We're the famous Tartan Army
Ooooooooh
Ooooooooh
Oooooh Scotland
Scotland
I'd walk a million miles
For one of your goals
Oh Scotland

WALES

Stand up if you hate England

Stand up if you hate England,
Stand up if you hate England,
The red dragon,
Would kill the rose,
Stand up if you hate England...

Oh fluffy sheep

(To the tune of 'When the saints go marching in')
Oh fluffy sheep,
Are wonderful,
Oh fluffy sheep are wonderful,
They are white, Welsh and fluffy
Oh fluffy sheep are wonderful.

Welsh not British! Welsh not British!

Welsh not British! Welsh not British!

Who needs Charlotte Church?

Who needs Charlotte Church?
When we've got Simon Church!
Who needs Charlotte Church?
When we've got Simon Church!

Shoes off! If you love Cymru!

Shoes off! If you love Cymru!
Shoes off! If you love Cymru!
Shoes off! If you love Cymru...

Always S*** on the English Side of the Bridge

Always s*** on the English side of the bridge,
De de, dededede dede,
Always s*** on the English side of the bridge,
De de, dededede dede...

Wembley's a Library

Wembley's a library,
Wembley's a library,
Wembley's a library,
Wembley's a library...

REPUBLIC OF IRELAND

In Dublin's fair city
In Dublin's fair city,
Where girls are so pretty,
I first set my eyes on sweet Molly Malone,
As she pushed her wheelbarrow
Through streets broad and narrow,
Crying, "Cockles and mussels, alive, alive oh"!

Chorus
Alive, alive oh! alive, alive oh!
Crying, "Cockles and mussels, alive, alive oh"!

Now she was a fishmonger,
And sure twas no wonder,
For so were her mother and father before,
And they each wheeled their barrow,
Through streets broad and narrow,
Crying, "Cockles and mussels, alive, alive oh"!

She died of a fever,
And no one could save her,
And that was the end of sweet Molly Malone.
Now her ghost wheels her barrow,
Through streets broad and narrow,
Crying, "Cockles and mussels, alive, alive oh"!

We've got Glenn Whelan

(To the Tune of 'I've Got a Feeling'
by the Black-eyed Peas)
We've got Glenn Whelan,
and tonight's gonna be a good night!

Whose that Playin' Like they're Brazil?

(Sang to the tune 'Is It A Monster')
Whose that playin' like they're Brazil?
Is it the England?
No it's the Ireland!

NORTHERN IRELAND

We hate England
We hate England,
We hate England,
We hate England more than you,
We hate England more than you...

Ulster till I die
Ulster till I die,
I'm Ulster till I die
I know I am,
I'm sure I am,
I'm Ulster till i die...

David Healy
He gets the ball, he scores a goal, Healy, Healy,
The little man from Killyleagh, Healy, Healy
He beat the England and the Spain,
Give him the ball, he'll do it again,
David Healy, Ulster's number 9...

A Goal
We nearly scored a goal,
We nearly scored a goal,
We nearly scored a goal,
A GOAL!

Are You England
Are You England
Are You England
Are You
Are You England in disguise
Are You England in disguise

ACKNOWLEDGEMENTS

Many thanks to all the football clubs, their fanzines
and supporters whose help was invaluable in producing
this compilation.

Special thanks to the following
Two Together, Barnet fanzine; Mick Gething and Ruth
Huggett, Bolton Wanderers Supporters Club (London);
The City Gent, Bradford City fanzine; Andrew Turton at
The Thin Blue Line, Cardiff City fanzine; Les Motherby at
Amber Nectar, Hull City fanzine; John "Marching On
Together" Hughes, Leeds United fanatic; *Dante Friend,*
The Independent Manchester City Fans' Line; *Fly Me To
The Moon,* Middlesbrough fanzine; Simon Sephton,
Scunthorpe United programme editor; Rob Offer's
Stadium of Light website and Kev Howard for their
Sunderland input; Gavin Mortimer, Tartan Army foot-
soldier; John "The Baggie" Owen, WBA fanatic; Xavier
Wiggins at *Hoof The Ball Up,* Wimbledon fanzine.

Apologies to anyone I've not mentioned.